GW00771160

BENET'S

ARTEFACTS OF ENGLAND & THE UNITED KINGDOM CURRENT VALUES

Medieval Edition 2015

Published by Greenlight Publishing

Written and Compiled by Brett Hammond

BENET'S ARTEFACTS
OF ENGLAND & THE UNITED KINGDOM
CURRENT VALUES
MEDIEVAL EDITION

Written and Compiled by:
Brett Hammond, CEO, TimeLine Auctions,
TimeLine Auctions Limited,
The Court House, 363 Main Road, Harwich,
Essex CO12 4DN, UK
Tel.: +44 (0) 1277 815121
Email: enquiries@timelineauctions.com
www.timelineauctions.com

Published by:
Greenlight Publishing, The Publishing House,
119 Newland Street, Witham, Essex CM8 1WF
Tel: 01376 521900
www.greenlightpublishing.co.uk

Origination by Christine Jennett

Cover by Damir Radić

ISBN 978-1-897738-58-0

All rights reserved. No part of this publication may be reproduced or transmitted in any form or by any means, electronic or mechanical, including photocopy, recording, computer scanning, or any information storage and retrieval system, without prior permission in writing from the publisher.

INTRODUCTION TO
THE MEDIEVAL EDITION

Welcome to the medieval edition of *Benet's Artefacts*, a handy visual guide to objects found in the United Kingdom and Europe.

Benet's Artefacts has been in print for more than a decade, and has come to be regarded as the encyclopaedia for UK metal detectorists. The first edition, issued in 2000, sold out very quickly and became a very sought-after title. The second edition was issued in 2003, and had twice as many colour photographs of artefacts included. It has since become a standard reference work for metal detectorists and others wishing to identify their finds. That book is now more than 10 years old and was in need of revision and expansion. The third edition met the needs of existing users and appealed to a new generation of detectorists, as it included many more objects and over 3,000 images. Now *Benet's Medieval* goes one step further by continuing the series, and providing even more images and values than ever before.

Benet's was from the outset a guide to current market prices, based on direct knowledge of the market for antiquities in the United Kingdom. Market prices change over time according to a number of factors, including the object's physical condition, its rarity, and the number of collectors who are likely to want to buy it. For these reasons, a complete revision of the published price ranges has been made.

Another factor that can affect price is accurate identification. Objects recorded with the Finds Liaison Officers of the Portable Antiquities Scheme are studied by professionals who have access to years of experience and large libraries of reference books. Obviously, the more objects recorded with the scheme, the more comprehensive its records become and thus items which appear rare and mysterious can be more easily identified.

The items photographed for this book have been chosen as a good cross-section of the material that can be found in the United Kingdom, but we have not aimed at publishing a full range of any particular object type or period. There are specialist books and magazine articles on most if not all artefact types, and the reader should consult them for detailed information. The number of examples published in these pages does not relate directly to rarity in the market.

Thank you for choosing *Benet's Artefacts*. We hope you find it useful and enjoyable!

CONTENTS

ACKNOWLEDGEMENTS

Benet's Medieval is the fourth book in a series of a work that has become a reference standard, and it is in many respects a team effort since I have had to rely on the skills and specialist knowledge of many people in compiling the final text and images.

First I wish to thank the TimeLine Auctions team for their invaluable assistance with this project. Special thanks are due to Michaela Simonova for her help in collating the material within this edition. I am grateful to Stephen Pollington, who assisted with the text and James Millership and Davor Radić who handled the photography and graphic compilation aspects of the project.

Images have been supplied from the archives of TimeLine Originals and TimeLine Auctions.

My greatest thanks are, as ever, due to my wife, Tanja, for all her moral support and hard work.

VALUES

The price ranges indicated in this book represent what a collector or museum might be prepared to pay, not what a dealer might offer.

The prices refer to the illustrated objects in the condition shown. If you have an artefact in better or worse condition, the price should be adjusted accordingly. The valuations are based on four criteria:-

1. Condition
2. Quality of Workmanship
3. Rarity
4. Demand

Generally, all other factors being equal, it is quality in design and execution that commands a premium. The highest standards of workmanship are rare and exceptional in any age; objects which display these qualities are always the most prized.

THE MEDIEVAL PERIOD

The 'medieval period' or Middle Ages covers the centuries from the Norman invasion in 1066 down to the end of the Tudor dynasty in 1603. The records of this period are comprehensive enough that we can both understand the politics of kings and archbishops and read the private communications of relatively humble merchants and landowners on a scale not possible for any earlier period.

The Norman invasion and the establishment of a French-speaking aristocracy changed permanently the relationship between the upper classes and those on whom they depended to work their lands and process the products. Although the Norman dynasty lasted less than a century, the crown's ties to France and the Holy Roman Empire were far-reaching. England was drawn into religious wars in the Near East (the Crusades) and lengthy and futile wars on the Continent (the Hundred Years' War) which benefitted only a few key families with landholdings on both sides of the Channel. Wars between England, Wales and Scotland occupied a large part of the earlier medieval period, followed by an invasion of Ireland. Rivalries within the English and Welsh aristocracies produced more bloodshed, and the period ended with an age of exploration and empire-building on the far shores of the Atlantic Ocean.

Literacy was a key factor in the medieval period, and despite the insistence on French for official record-keeping and court procedures, English remained the language of the people of England (and Welsh for Wales). Therefore it is not unusual to find both languages represented in inscriptions in this period. Spelling was not fixed until much later, so variation in word-forms reflects local dialects. Aids to teaching, such as hornbooks, played a major part in spreading literacy while ampullae and pilgrim badges show that religious devotion was important.

Another highly visual medieval phenomenon is heraldry – originally a means of instant visual recognition for the battlefield which in time became a sophisticated system to indicate ancestry and affiliation. Using a combination of heraldic information and dating by technique and style, it is sometimes possible to assign an object to a particular family and even an individual. This opens up a broad field for discovery and interpretation of artefacts.

Medieval objects range in quality and rarity, and the majority of them are avidly collected. Heraldic and ecclesiastical items such as horse-harness mounts and seal matrices are among the more obvious collectibles. Weapons such as bullock daggers and hand-guns are also popular. A sudden surge in interest in hawking rings and vervels saw prices leap more than 500% in recent years at TimeLine Auctions. From the Tudor period, even relatively humble items such as dress pins, tags, and belt fittings survive in sufficient quantity to form the basis of a comprehensive collection.

BLADES AND TOOLS

Weapons, domestic tools and cutlery form a broad range of items which are well represented in the remains of the medieval period.

Swords were the primary weapon of the nobility, used on the battlefield but also worn as symbol of status. The scabbards and belts were often provided with elaborate fittings which added to the splendour of the weapon itself. Swords can often be dated by developments in the shape of the pommel and crossguard.

Bowmanship was important during the medieval period for warfare as well as for food. Iron arrowheads could be provided with a tang (shank) or tapering socket and the cutting edges formed in a variety of shapes for specific purposes. The iron heads of crossbow bolts comprised a tubular socket and a square-section point. Mace heads were formed as a tubular socket with flanges and spikes for maximum penetration of plate armour.

Spearheads continued their development from leaf-shaped types with modifications to the cross-section to provide rigidity. The attachment was most often by a split socket secured with a pin, but closed socket and tanged types were in use.

Axes (and variations such as halberds and voulges) were a standard battlefield weapon used to bring down horsemen and to deal with steel plate armour. Outside military applications, axes remained in use for forestry purposes, for woodworking and carpentry.

Knives ranged from humble tools and tableware to elaborate items worn for display; daggers likewise show a variety of forms for military purposes and hunting.

Collectors of military equipment often acquire maces, spearheads, sword pommels and arrowheads as an inexpensive and interesting aspect of their subject area, while the range of arrowhead types can form the basis of a specialist collection. Axeheads are collected by military enthusiasts and also form an important part of a specialist collection of tools. Complete swords and sets of scabbard fittings are a rarity.

AX-52332
Bearded
Axehead
84mm
Hooked blade,
body decorated
with punched
squares.
£100 - £150

AX-7340
Axehead
160mm
Iron blade with
trident maker's
mark.
£50 - £80

AX-1348
Axehead
200mm
Broad iron
blade with
square socket.
£50 - £80

AX-45301
Bearded Axehead
120mm
Iron blade with tubular socket.
£50 - £80

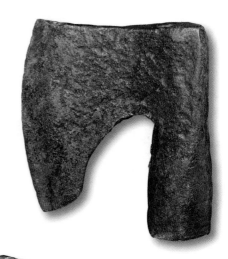

AH-2348
Arrowhead
125mm
Iron, 'fire-arrow'
type.
£100 - £150

AH-20319
Arrowheads
90 -120mm
Iron, with tangs
and sockets.
£10 - £20 each

AH-45586
Arrowhead Pair
130 -185mm
One a swallowtail
with twisted
shank, the
other with three
triangular points.
£80 - £120

AH-24673
Crossbow Bolts
67-74mm
Iron, pyramidal
points and square-
section shafts.
£20 each

OI-48140
Crossbow
Spanning Hook
140mm
Hook flat on one
side, loop above.
From £100

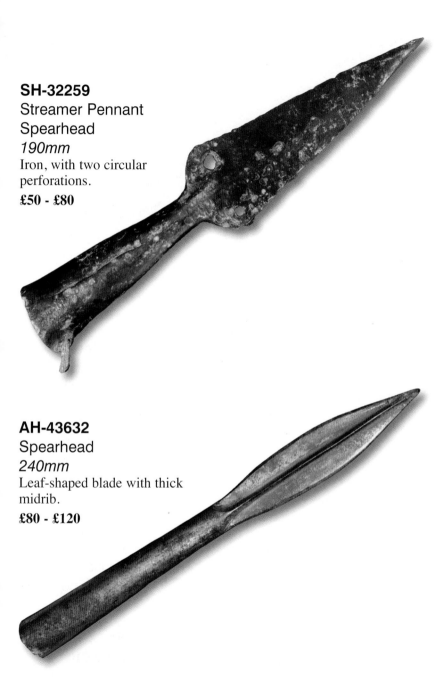

SH-32259
Streamer Pennant
Spearhead
190mm
Iron, with two circular
perforations.
£50 - £80

AH-43632
Spearhead
240mm
Leaf-shaped blade with thick
midrib.
£80 - £120

AH-47286
Spearhead
395mm
Leaf-shaped
blade with collar.
£80 - £120

AH-47285
Spearhead
285mm
Collar with loops,
European type.
£80 - £120

AH-51513
Spearhead
290mm
Triangular blade,
thick midrib.
£50 - £80

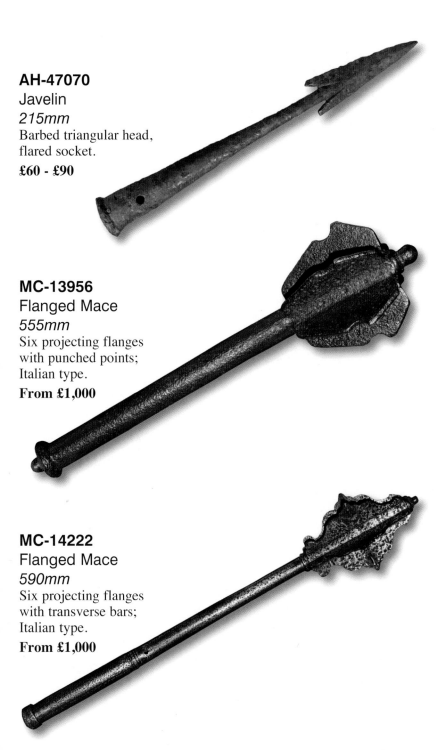

AH-47070
Javelin
215mm
Barbed triangular head,
flared socket.
£60 - £90

MC-13956
Flanged Mace
555mm
Six projecting flanges
with punched points;
Italian type.
From £1,000

MC-14222
Flanged Mace
590mm
Six projecting flanges
with transverse bars;
Italian type.
From £1,000

MC-40655
Mace Head
69mm
Raised lozenge projections.
£80 - £120

MC-20711
Morning Star Mace
Head
66mm
Four pyramidal projections
and circular socket.
£120 - £180

MC-26400
Morning Star Mace
Head
67mm
Four pyramidal projections
and circular socket.
£80 - £120

MC-46574
Morning Star Macehead
78mm
Four large pyramidal
projections.
£80 - £120

SW-51628
Baselard Sword
745mm
Animal-head
pommel, one side
showing a fiery
comet with rays
and tail.
From £5,000

SW-50600
Arming Sword
810mm
Wooden grip,
bulb pommel
with stud.
From £500

PM-48519
Gilt Chape
46mm
Folded with hatched detail,
Norman type.
£40 - £60

PM-44863
Gold Dagger Chape
15mm
Applied granule border with
green hardstone cloison.
£800 - £1,200

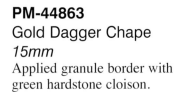

PM-52874
Sword Pommel
44mm
Facetted faces.
£40 - £60

PM-46268
Dagger Pommel
27mm
Barrel-shaped,
cockerel with human
head.
£100 - £150

PM-49831
Pommel
50mm
Quatrefoil motifs.
£50 - £80

PM-T0151
Sword Pommel
50mm
Oakeshott's Type F.
From £1,000

SW-45506
Arming Sword
Blade
870mm
With square
tip and abrupt
shoulders.
From £150

SW-5953
Iron Sword
1110mm
Disc-pommel
type.
From £1,000

PM-4755
Sword Pommel
36mm
Openwork type.
From £1,000

PM-T0150
Heraldic Sword
Pommel
34mm
Crusader period type.
£300 - £500

PM-42014
Sword
Pommel
65mm
Oakeshott's
type H.
£100 - £150

PM-38738
Sword Pommel
31mm
Inlaid niello U-shapes
and vertical lines with
pellet finials.
£20 - £30

PM-T0149
Dagger Pommel
65mm
Discoid with domed
face.
£30 - £50

PM-1350
Dagger Pommel
30mm
Four hatched panels.
£40 - £60

PM-T0152
Openwork Fitting
26mm
Pommel or sceptre finial.
£50 - £80

DC-41500
Silver-Gilt Dagger
Chape
28mm
Lion of England
trampling the thistle of
Scotland.
From £1,000

DC-T0153
Dagger Chape
42mm
Openwork advancing
lion motif; Norman
type.
£200 - £300

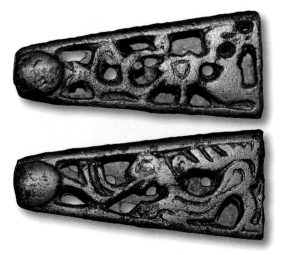

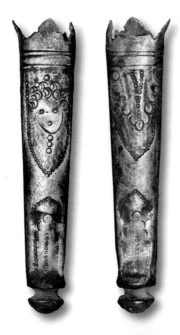

DC-4971
Silver Dagger Chape
59mm
Crenellated top and punched-point detail.
£80 - £120

DC-T0154
Dagger Chape
35mm
Fleur-de-lys design.
£50 - £80

DC-15751
Dagger Chape
35mm
Mounted knight in a helm amid foliage; Norman type.
£50 - £80

BC-T0155
Belt Chape
28mm
Facing birds motif.
£40 - £60

DS-46210
Miniature Dagger
Scabbard
58mm
Filigree and rosettes
to each face.
£50 - £80

KF-38160
Figural Knife Handle
34mm
Incised noblewoman in robe and
wimple supporting a castle tower.
£100 - £150

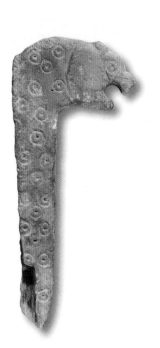

KF-42776
Knife with
Iconographic
Handle
190mm
Virgin Mary and
infant Jesus to
one face, St Peter
holding key and
chalice to the other.
£300 - £400

KF-40037
Folding Knife
Handle
57mm
Incised ring-and-dot
motifs, beast-head
finial with open
jaws; Norman type.
£80 - £120

KF-16408
Knife with Calligraphic Silver Fittings
230mm
Blade stamped 'V' and 'II' marks; wooden handle with reserved niello text bands '+BAUTHIOR+OR' above and '+MALCI+IAN[.] PAR' naming the three Magi (Balthazar, Melchior and Caspar).
From £500

KF-42778
Iconographic Knife
195mm
To one face, Adam and Eve by the tree of Knowledge of Good and Evil with serpent in the branches, to the other face a bearded male in a tunic.
£200 - £300

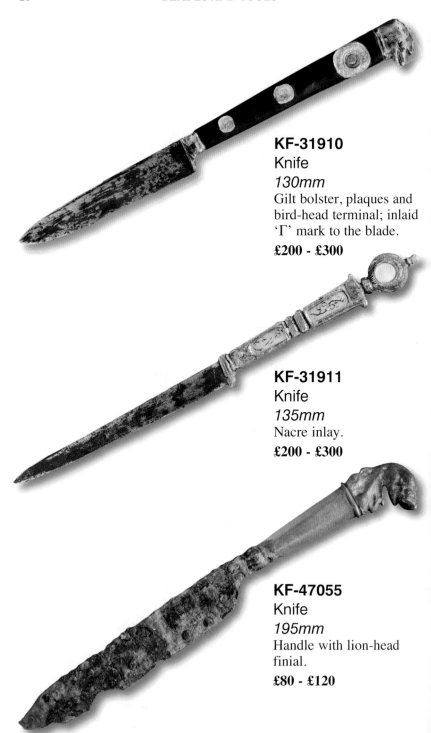

KF-31910
Knife
130mm
Gilt bolster, plaques and
bird-head terminal; inlaid
'Γ' mark to the blade.
£200 - £300

KF-31911
Knife
135mm
Nacre inlay.
£200 - £300

KF-47055
Knife
195mm
Handle with lion-head
finial.
£80 - £120

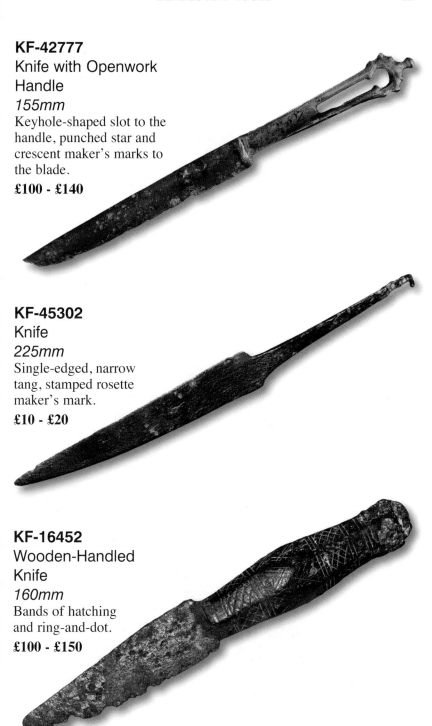

KF-42777
Knife with Openwork Handle
155mm
Keyhole-shaped slot to the handle, punched star and crescent maker's marks to the blade.
£100 - £140

KF-45302
Knife
225mm
Single-edged, narrow tang, stamped rosette maker's mark.
£10 - £20

KF-16452
Wooden-Handled Knife
160mm
Bands of hatching and ring-and-dot.
£100 - £150

KF-4733
Knife
180mm
Rectangular maker's
mark to the blade;
Tudor type.
£100 - £150

KF-4735
Knife
160mm
Plait-handled type;
Tudor type.
£100 - £150

KF-11449
Bone-Hilted
Hunting Knife
440mm
Leaf-shaped blade
with trefoil stop;
German type.
£80 - £120

KF-13738
Butcher Knife Blade
320mm
Thickened back and
rectangular-section tang.
£30 - £50

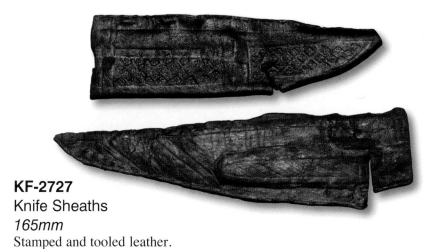

KF-2727
Knife Sheaths
165mm
Stamped and tooled leather.
£50 - £80 each

OI-45069
Caltrops
33-51mm
Leaf-shaped points
From £40 each

OI-51942
Caltrops
44-45mm
Leaf-shaped points.
From £40 each

OI-49932
Hand Cannon
270mm
Stamped heraldic
shield maker's
mark.
£100 - £150

OI-49931
Hand Cannon
330mm
Octagonal section, crescents
with pellets and crossed keys
maker's mark.
£100 - £150

OI-49930
Hand Cannon
305mm
Octagonal section.
£100 - £150

TimeLine Auctions

We are accepting single entries and collections of coins and antiquities

Bronze Age Gold Bracelet

Central London
Auction Venue

TimeLine Auctions Limited
The Court House
363 Main Road
Harwich, Essex
CO12 4DN

www.timelineauctions.com

+44 [0]1277 815121
enquiries@timelineauctions.com

BROOCHES, FASTENERS AND BUCKLES

Medieval brooches ranged from humble clothes fasteners cast in bronze through to highly ornate items of jewellery in gold and silver-gilt. Popular types were the annular ring-brooches and the earlier figural plaques which developed into pilgrim badges. Brooches made from coins also occur, taking advantage of the religious imagery of the cross element in the coin's design. On annular brooches, the outer face often included a band of text of a religious nature.

Clothes fasteners generally took the form of hook-and-eye sets provided with loops to sew onto the garment. Although many were rather plain, the more ornate types were highly decorative, made in gold or silver or with enamelled heraldic imagery. At the end of the medieval period, Tudor styles were introduced with substantial hooks, the plates formed in filigree and silver-gilt, in distinctive shapes based on formal arrangements of domes, granules and rosettes.

Medieval buckles developed into a range of forms including single loop and double loop types, with or without a plate attached to the leather or fabric belt or strap. The loops range from simple rings through kidney-shapes to ornate forms with human faces. The plate could be as simple as a folded bronze sheet to as complex as a cast openwork form with religious, military, heraldic and other imagery.

Brooches are often collected for their physical beauty and for technical aspects of their production, as well as for their social and religious significance. Buckles, fasteners and clasps of various types are also collected for their own sake, as well as forming part of period-specific (e.g. Crusades, Tudor) and type-specific (e.g. garment-hook, heraldic mount) collections.

MB-3277
Gold Annular Brooch
29mm
Inset cabochon garnets and sapphires.
From £3,000

MB-7799
Silver-Gilt Annular Brooch
37mm
Eight blue cloisons.
£300 - £500

MB-17268
Silver Annular Brooch
19mm
Enigmatic inscription '+au bodies li uuialls' and 'VIIII' to the underside.
£200 - £300

MB-2864
Silver Annular
Brooch
64mm
With lozenge plaques.
£300 - £500

MB-27610
Silver Annular
Brooch
51mm
Ropework with
openwork beaded
surround.
From £500

MB-2350
Silver Annular Brooch
20mm
Clasped hands motif,
inscribed to both faces.
£100 - £150

MB-2708
Silver-Gilt Annular
Brooch
28mm
Quatrefoil elements
inscribed 'ESON[?]IA[?]'.
£80 - £120

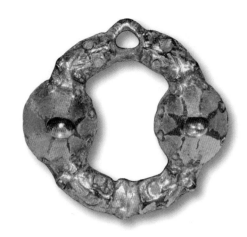

MB-16493
Silver-Gilt Annular
Brooch
16mm
Cabochon amethysts and
dogs' heads.
£200 - £300

MB-44895
Silver-Gilt Annular
Brooch
42mm
Expanding cross motifs,
pin with thistle-head detail.
£200 - £300

MB-38696
Silver Annular Brooch
19mm
Profile animal-heads and
masks; Norman type.
£100 - £150

MB-31744
Silver-Gilt Annular
Brooch
16mm
Opposed beast-heads.
£50 - £80

MB-31232
Silver-Gilt Annular
Brooch
15mm
Beast-heads with ribbed
collars.
£50 - £80

MB-2577
Silver Annular Brooch
42mm
With lozengiform plaques.
£100 - £150

MB-2297
Silver Annular Brooch
27mm
Heart with decorative escutcheon.
£100 - £150

MB-26460
Silver-Gilt Annular
Brooch
29mm
Lozengiform panels
with saltires.
£80 - £120

MB-6275
Silver-Gilt Annular Brooch
21mm
Floral motifs modelled as praying
hands.
£20 - £30

MB-4661
Silver Annular Brooch
49mm
Openwork with studs.
£50 - £80

MB-3405
Silver Annular Brooch
21mm
Pellets and ropework
decoration.
£50 - £80

MB-7975
Silver Annular Brooch
32mm
Punched-point wreath
detail.
£40 - £60

MB-49069
Inscribed Annular Brooch
60mm
Enigmatic inscription between
two inscribed lines
£100 - £150

MB-48514
Annular Posy Brooch
15mm
Silver annular brooch
with blundered legend
'AMOLVNICITOMNA' for
'amor vincit omnia' (love
conquers all).
£200 - £300

MB-49061
Splayed Eagle Badge
36mm
Bird with wings extended, body
with cross-hatched feather texture
£100 - £150

MB-52215
Gilt Filigree Brooch
23mm
Gilt metal cell, filigree and granule detailing, inset glass 'gemstone'.
£80 - £120

MB-52210
Gilt Disc Brooch
18mm
Silver with gilt repoussé details.
£40 - £60

MB-48234
Gilt Annular Brooch
14mm
Silver parcel-gilt with crescents.
£20 - £30

MB-52212
Penannular Brooch
26mm
Domed finials; European type.
£30 - £40

MB-52870
Bird Brooch
36mm
Bird with spread wings and fan tail. Norman type.
£80 - £120

MB-43751
Gold Royal Monogram Badge
13mm
Gold 'KR' monogram badge of Charles VIII of France.
£80 - £120

MB-2239
Annular Brooch
34mm
Gilt-bronze with
lion masks and cells;
Romanesque type.
£150 - £200

MB-45505
Annular Brooch
41mm
Gilt-bronze with pelleted
border and rosette.
£80 - £120

MB-4203
Epigraphic
Annular Brooch
50mm
With enigmatic
'+eudiobeneh'oal'
inscription in
blackletter.
£50 - £80

MB-41932
Annular Brooch
37mm
With animal decoration.
£30 - £50

MB-52462
Annular Brooch
48mm
A flat-section plaque
with rim to the centre,
band of ring-and-dot
motifs.
£80 - £120

MB-8370
Annular Brooch
40mm
With trefoil branches,
punched pellet decoration.
£30 - £50

MB-41931
Annular Brooch
34mm
Scrolled foliage
decoration.
£30 - £50

MB-41930
Annular Brooch
40mm
Figure-of-eight
decoration.
£30 - £50

MB-15040
Gold Ring Brooch
17mm
Triangular-section pin.
£400 - £600

MB-18122
Gold Ring Brooch
10mm
Rosette to the pin.
£80 - £120

MB-7974
Silver-Gilt Ring
Brooch
23mm
Ropework ornament.
£30 - £50

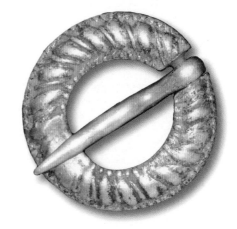

MB-18123
Silver-Gilt Ring Brooch
19mm
Chain hoop.
£40 - £60

MB-13035
Silver-Gilt Coin
Brooch
19mm
Edward I penny with
green glass cabochons.
£100 - £150

MB-2238
Ring Brooch
16mm
Inscribed 'Amor Vincit
Omnia' (Love conquers
all).
£150 - £200

MB-19620
Ring Brooch
33mm
With enigmatic inscription.
£50 - £80

MB-T0100
Openwork Brooch
27mm
Angel and beast
confronted, human mask
between; Norman type.
£100 - £150

MB-21555
Openwork Brooch
30mm
With pairs of bird-heads.
£30 - £50

CF-T0112
Silver-Gilt Hat Pin
21mm
With religious text.
£400 - £600

CF-30034
Silver-Gilt Clothes
Fastener
24mm
Coin of Margaret of
Constantinople with
loop and hook.
£100 - £150

CF-8579
Silver-Gilt Clothes
Fastener
27mm
Robed figure next to
scrolled foliage.
£150 - £200

CF-41946
Silver-Gilt Bird
Hook Fastener
27mm
D-section hooked
mount, bird finial
with raised head.
£50 - £80

CF-40322
Heraldic Cloak Fastener
31mm
Enamelled bronze heater-shaped plaque with
arms of Robert Tipetot.
£100 - £150

CF-31236
Silver-Gilt Fastener
31mm
Tudor type.
£80 - £120

CF-30332
Silver-Gilt
Fastener
19mm
Tudor type.
£40 - £60

GC-T0124
Garment Clasp
15mm
Disc with three
loops, filigree rim
and annulets.
£50 - £80

GC-52426
Belt Hook
58mm
S-shaped fastener
with zoomorphic
heads.
£80 - £120

CF-52506
Silver Livery Pin
68mm
Lion statant gardant with Samson
on its back.
£100 - £150

GC-T0125
Hooked Clasp
23mm
Tudor type.
£50 - £80

CF-45166
Gilt Pin
Terminal
16mm
Silver-gilt, bird
with wings
partly spread.
£50 - £80

CF-46239
Belt Link
32mm
Female mask with
hair to the sides
£40 - £60

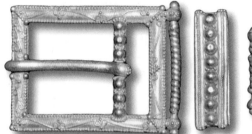

BB-37898
Gold Belt Buckle Suite
29-53mm
Matching set with filigree detailing and rosette.
From £2,000

BB-19304
Silver-Gilt Belt Buckle Suite
85-120mm
With stylised face, addorsed geese and central rosette.
From £500

BB-22294
Silver Buckle
and Jewelled
Plate
50mm
Low-relief
floral motifs and
central blue glass
cabochon.
£50 - £80

BB-27769
Silver Buckle and
Plate
38mm
Kidney-shaped loop with
tremello border.
£50 - £80

BB-6724
Silver Buckle and Plate
71mm
Articulated, with D-shaped loop.
£80 - £120

BB-11160
Silver Belt
Buckle
58mm
Rosette motif
to the plate.
£80 - £120

BB-24451
Crown-
Shaped
Buckle
62mm
With serrated
forward edge
and triangular
projections.
£50 - £80

BB-23329
Buckle
49mm
Scrolled foliage
ornament;
Siculo-Norman
type.
£10 - £20

BB-18112
Decorated
Buckle
45mm
Notched
profile.
£20 - £30

BB-T0102
Heraldic Belt
Buckle
48mm
Enamelled
ornament;
Romanesque style.
£100 - £150

BP-T0103
Heraldic Belt
Plate
45mm
Lions rampant motif.
£300 - £500

BP-46628
Belt Plate
43mm
Armed warrior motif.
£300 - £500

BP-19289
Limoges Buckle
Plate
36mm
With mounted knight
motif.
£150 - £200

BP-T0101
Buckle Plate
41mm
Cockatrice motif.
£100 - £150

BP-27534
Enamelled Buckle Plate
41mm
Gilt-bronze, bird on blue field.
£100 - £150

BB-52115
Buckle
60mm
Tongue-shaped plaque;
Byzantine type.
£50 - £80

BB-52114
Buckle
73mm
Tongue-shaped openwork
plaque; Byzantine type.
£100 - £150

BB-50840
Strap End
91mm
Scrolled motifs;
Byzantine type.
£50 - £80

BB-50847
Heraldic Harpy
Belt Plate
30mm
White enamel panel,
reserved bird with a
crowned woman's
head carrying a torch.
£50 - £80

We are accepting single entries and collections of coins and antiquities

Viking Scandinavian Equal-Arm Brooch

Central London
Auction Venue

TimeLine Auctions Limited
The Court House
363 Main Road
Harwich, Essex
CO12 4DN

www.timelineauctions.com

+44 [0]1277 815121
enquiries@timelineauctions.com

DOMESTIC ITEMS

In this section we include a range of everyday and commonplace items which nevertheless have considerable significance in terms of the social history for which they provide evidence, and value to collectors with an interest in the medieval period.

Barrel locks in bronze were often created in the form of animals or bear identification text. Casket and other small keys were used in conjunction with padlocks in every household to keep small valuables secure. Weights and balances (tumbrels) formed part of the routine equipment of merchants and tradesmen needing to establish the quality of coinage – the coin places on the tipping paddle will weight it down and slide off if of the correct weight, but stay on the scale if clipped or excessively worn.

Ceramic floor tiles with figural decoration or religious imagery formed part of the establishment of wealthy households; other ceramic items include jugs, pitchers, plates, goblets, cups and various glazed wares. The very wealthy included their heraldry in the decoration of such items as a show of status and probably to prevent theft. Metal and wooden spoons were common domestic items which survive rarely; the metal ones often retain their decoration and in some cases the maker's mark. Likewise humble bronze thimbles were used by seamstresses and the forms vary little over the centuries until modern times.

Iron spurs of both the earlier prick and later rowel types were worn by nobles, warriors and huntsmen. Cockspurs were used as part of the betting game of cockfighting.

Medieval domestic items seldom have the splendour of other medieval artefacts but the social history implications make them very attractive to collectors.

MK-T0126
Key
99mm
Trefoil bow type.
£100 - £150

MK-26423
Openwork Key
55mm
Openwork quatrefoil
handle, copper inlay
to each face.
£100 - £150

MK-21554
Barrel-Lock Key
66mm
Lozengiform bow.
£40 - £60

MK-43789
Folding Casket
Key
57mm
Hinged bow with
quatrefoil void.
£40 - £60

MK-T0125
Casket Key
41mm
Trefoil bow type.
£20 - £30

MK-53320
Door Key
100mm
Barrel shank, bow with beast-head detail.
£150 - £200

MK-52010
'Daniel and the Lion' Key Bow
89mm
Openwork bow with the prophet Daniel confronting the lion, Romanesque style.
£150 - £200

MK-47281
Key
175mm
Looped bow with knop.
£20 - £30

MK-43399
Door Key
105mm
Trefoil bow.
£80 - £120

MK-44896
Key
67mm
Tubular shank,
openwork handle
with monogram.
£50 - £80

ML-45250
Horse Barrel
Lock
45mm
Galloping horse with
saddle and bridle.
£80 - £120

ML-11197
Inscribed Barrel
Lock
33mm
Inscribed text
'VISIVM VIVAS'
('... that thou may
live') in regular
Roman capitals.
£50 - £80

ML-18377
Horse Lock
46mm
Horse with saddle
and reins; Siculo-
Norman type.
£80 - £120

ML- 44925
Lion-Headed Lock Plate
57mm
Beast-head with lentoid eyes and notched fringe;
Norman type.
£80 - £120

ML-1126
Padlock
46mm
Sliding
panel to
the keyhole.
£50 - £80

ML-13678
Padlock Pair
35-54mm
A group of two
bronze padlocks,
one with hinged
loop and sliding
cover plate to the
reverse, the other
with carinated band.
£50 - £80

ML-T0127
Combination Lock
32mm
Five-ring type, Tudor.
£200 – £300

ML-T0128
Combination Lock
19mm
Five-ring type, Tudor.
£100 - £200

ML-52207
Letter Combination
Padlock
20mm
Barrel-shaped
combination padlock with
five tumblers and locating
letters on the frame.
£300 - £400

ML-51126
Money Box
190mm
Iron box with reinforced edges
and coin slot.
£400 - £600

ML-51516
Padlock and
Key
150mm
Barrel-shaped
padlock and
push key with
slot.
£80 - £120

OI-7356
Floor Tile
120mm
Ceramic tile with yellow
glaze, quarter-circle with
Lombardic 'M', heater shield
and blackletter script 'Intr
dns' (for '... dominus').
£80 - £120

OI-30335
Laver Spout
62mm
Dog's head with
pipe issuing from
the mouth.
£30 - £40

OI-52873
'Westminster'
Floor Tile
110mm
Ceramic, white
rosette on red field.
From £100

OI-46452
Glazed Skillet
300mm
Green-glazed,
pouring lip to the
rim.
£40 - £60

OI-51501
Firesteel
66mm
Iron shoe,
bronze
handle with
horses.
£80 - £120

OI-42779
Candlestick with Lion Feet
305mm
Drip-tray with three L-shaped feet,
each a sitting lion figure.
From £1,000

OI-44846
Ornamented Bowl
48mm
Band of ornament in panels showing
birds and other subjects against a
hatched background.
£150 - £200

OI-46453
Glazed Tripod
Skillet
245mm
Green-glazed, three
stub feet, pouring lip
to the rim.
£40 - £60

SP-12814
Silver-Gilt Spoon
150mm
'Diamond Point'
finial.
From £1,000

SP-21053
Silver Spoon
150mm
Hexagonal diamond-
point finial.
From £500

SP-38662
Silver Spoon
150mm
'Diamond Point' finial, stamped mark to rear of the handle.
From £500

SP-12567
Apostle Spoon
120mm
D-section handle with robed standing figure.
£100 - £150

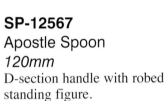

SP-1157
Bowl and Spoon
165mm
Sycamore wood.
From £500

HR-46624
Silver Heraldic Hawking Ring
9mm
Band inscribed 'OF HITCHIN' (Hertfordshire), heraldic shield with crest of a dexter hand, initials 'T M' above.
From £500

FR-45986
Gilt Falconry Ring
27mm
Trumpet bezel with intaglio bird of prey seizing a smaller bird.
£100 - £150

HR-47894
Falconry Leash Swivel
28mm
Rotating swivel with hatching, Norman type
£40 - £60

HR-47045
Swivel
25mm
Cross cleché to two faces
£20 - £30

HR-44889
Strap Junction
Finial
34mm
Beast-heads with swivel mount below
£50 - £80

SU-9270
Silver Cock Spur
28mm
Initialled 'WP'.
£100 - £150

SU-31217
Silver Cock Spur
39mm
Five holes for
attachment.
£80 - £120

SU-26753
Silver Cock-
Fighting Spur
35mm
Twelve perforations
for attachment.
£80 - £120

SU-47483
Spurs
70-100mm
Prick spurs with
pierced ends.
From £10 each

SU-4692
Prick Spur
150mm
Short pricket with collar to rear. Late Saxon or Norman type.
£100 - £150

SU-4688
Prick Spur
140mm
Triangular-section bow and attachment rivets for leather straps.
£80 - £120

SU-38453
Norman Spur Buckle
with Wolf's Head
33mm
Hound's or wolf's head
modelled in the round to
one end. Norman type.
£10 - £20

OI-48529
Saddle Pommel Cap
54mm
Radiating ribs, scrolls and
punched circles.
£50 - £80

SD-6274
Folding Pocket
Sundial
25mm
With folding triangular
gnomon; engraved on the
upper face with two series
of numerals.
£200 - £300

TH-1354
Silver Thimble
28mm
Inscribed AMORE
VINCIT OMNIA 'Love
conquers all'; Tudor type.
£400 - £600

WT-81
Armorial Steelyard Weight
70mm
Lead-filled latten weight, three incised heater shields of arms of England (three lions passant); the Hanseatic merchants (double-headed eagle) and Richard or his son Edmund, Earls of Cornwall and Poitou (lion rampant).
From £500

WT-45248
Steelyard Weight with Horse and Lion
52mm
Prancing horse in high-relief and similar panel with a rampant gardant lion to the reverse; Eastern European type.
£200 - £300

WT-28021
Panther Steelyard Weight
44mm
Head of a panther with
open mouth, pecked surface
indicating spots.
£50 - £80

WT-1790
Steelyard Weight
72mm
Raised identification mark on
the shoulder.
£50 - £80

WT-52219
Steelyard Weight
65mm
Lead-filled, rings to the
shoulder.
£50 - £80

WT-4283
Seated Figure
Weight
51mm
Seated male philosopher
in a loose toga and tunic.
£200 - £300

WT-30305 (M18-0303)
Nested Cup Weight
Set
41mm
Amsterdam issue type.
£100 - £150

WT-44454
Large Trade Weight
60mm
Stamped crown symbol to
one face.
£50 - £80

WT-1049
Trade Weight
69mm
Crown and Fleur de Lys
type
£60 - £90

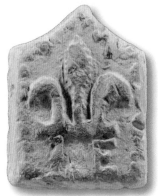

WT-4218
Lead 'Lis' Trade
Weight
63mm
Fleur-de-lis motif above
the initials 'IE'.
£30 - £50

WT-31970
Lead Heraldic Trade
Weight
72mm
Heater shield with three
lions passant gardant in
the field.
£20 - £30

WT-20344
Lead Face Trade
Weight
45mm
Male face with domed
cap.
£20 - £30

WT-T0115
Coin Weight
15mm
Antwerp Gold
Burgundian Ducat
1567.
£10 - £20

WT-21722
Tumbrel
60mm
Vertical stand with
saltire and ring-and-
dot motifs, pivoted
arm.
£100 - £150

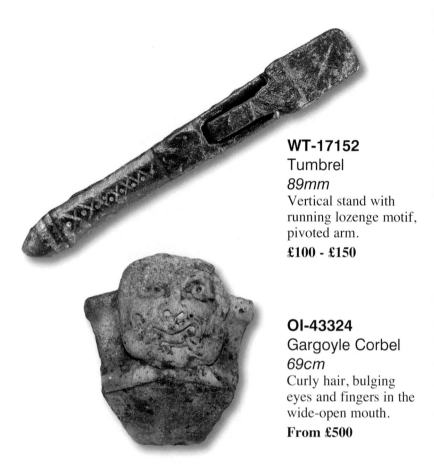

WT-17152
Tumbrel
89mm
Vertical stand with running lozenge motif, pivoted arm.
£100 - £150

OI-43324
Gargoyle Corbel
69cm
Curly hair, bulging eyes and fingers in the wide-open mouth.
From £500

OI-43332
Jeweller's Hammer
170mm
With flat striking face.
£80 - £120

Timeline Auctions

We are accepting single entries and collections of coins and antiquities

Iceni - Antedios - Triple Moon Gold Stater

Central London
Auction Venue

TimeLine Auctions Limited
The Court House
363 Main Road
Harwich, Essex
CO12 4DN

www.timelineauctions.com

+44 [0]1277 815121
enquiries@timelineauctions.com

FINGER RINGS

Finger rings were an important and symbolic piece of jewellery in the medieval period. Many featured text of a religious nature, or a romantic declaration of love. Others are inscribed with enigmatic text, probably amuletic or magical, as well as geometric symbols.

Inset gemstones such as garnet and sapphire were often used to add sparkle and vivid colour. Beaded borders, engraved scrolls and foliage all added interest to the hoop.

Later versions confined the message to the inner face as a secret known only to the wearer, but many medieval rings display the text on the outer face. The popular 'mane in fede' (hands in good faith) motif dates back to Roman times, but occurs widely on rings meant to confirm a compact, agreement or betrothal.

Signet rings were engraved with a personal motif, often heraldic in nature, for use as a seal matrix on documents. Although associated with royal officers and churchmen, merchants and other men of wealth also possessed seal rings. By the end of the period, standardised designs became available, pre-cut for personalisation.

Archer's rings arose from the need to protect the thumb when using a bow. In certain styles of archery, the thumb is hooked around the bowstring below the arrow and the arrow is held with the forefinger. The bowstring is held tight against the archer's thumb and the flange on the ring protects the thumb when the bowstring is drawn and released.

The triangular flange is often decorated with scrolled foliage and geometric ornament. The hoop is generally flat in section with minimal detailing to the outer face. Bronze rings are the standard type but occasional examples are known in silver and rarely in gold.

Finger rings are popular with jewellery collectors due to the wide range of types available and the intrinsic interest of the heraldic and other symbols. Archer's rings are popular with both rings collectors and with militaria collectors.

FR-47535
Gold Decorated Posy
Ring
17mm
Rosettes and fronds to the
outer face, 'de bon coer'
([be] of good heart) in
blackletter script.

From £800

FR-53327
Silver Decorated Posy Ring
20mm
Incised cross potent and scrolled foliage
tendrils, blackletter text 'tu et escrip mon
cuer' (you are written on my heart).

From £300

FR-43349
Gold Decorated Posy Ring
17mm

Blackletter text to the outer face 'mon *
cuer * ane' and to the inner face 'bien le
garder' (my heart's ring - guard it well).

From £500

FR-31578
Gold Inscribed Posy Ring
21mm

With three bands of text.

From £5,000

FR-36346
Gold Inscribed Posy
Ring
23mm
Legend in seriffed capitals
'+AM*ORVI*NCIT*IOMI'
(amor vincit omnia: 'love
conquers all') and
'+IE*SVII*CIEN*LIVD' (ie
sui ici en lieu: 'I am here in
place (of a lover)'.
From £2,000

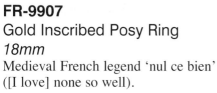

FR-9907
Gold Inscribed Posy Ring
18mm
Medieval French legend 'nul ce bien'
([I love] none so well).
£1,000 - £1500

FR-8645
Gold Inscribed Posy Ring
19mm
Engraved flowers separating blackletter
text ' + en bon an' (a good year).
£1,000 - £1,500

FR-3611
Gold Inscribed Posy Ring
19mm
Engraved star and flower decoration and
'en bon amour' (for good love); on the
inner face the text 'en bon an' (a good
year).
From £1,000

FR-7640
Gold Inscribed Posy Ring
18mm
Blackletter text 'Joie Honour Joie' (joy-honour-joy)
inlaid in white enamel.
From £1,000

FR-35702
Gold Inscribed Posy Ring
19mm
Inscribed 'ioy de mondesir' (joy of my desire)
and rosette marking the incipit.
From £1,000

FR-1480
Gold Inscribed Posy Ring
16mm
Inscription in black letter script
'DVNTRE E JOYE' (? and joy).
From £1,000

FR-30088
Gold Inscribed Posy Ring
13mm
Reserved lettering against a hatched
background 'ave', 'du', 'aie'.
£800 - £1,200

FR-30363
Gold Inscribed Posy Ring
20mm
Inscribed 'vous et nul autre' (you and none other).
From £800

FR-30367
Gold Inscribed Posy Ring
18mm
Flower-and-stalk ornament, blackletter text
'nul ce bien' ([I love] none so well).
From £800

FR-3453
Gold Inscribed Posy Ring
17mm
Blackletter script with foliage
motifs 'mon coer aves' (have
my heart).
£400 - £600

FR-38669
Gold Double Inscribed
Posy Ring
16mm
Internal inscription 'ego.sum.
via.veritas.et.vita' and external
inscription 'I am the way, the
truth, and the + life', its English
translation, quotation from John
14:16.
£500 - £800

FR-19774
Gold Inscribed Posy Ring
19mm
Inscribed 'hEhEchGohvAmiEVAmVehANS:'
in Lombardic script.
£500 - £800

FR-2341
Gold Inscribed Posy Ring
18mm
Inscribed externally +seet '·leale '·efei '·teneia
(be ever loyal and hold ...) in Lombardic script.
From £500

FR-3456
Gold Inscribed Figural Ring
21mm

Engraved image of Christ's face, vinescroll motifs and the text '+IESUSNAZARENUS' (Jesus of Nazareth) in Lombardic script and 'CASPAR * MELCHIOR * BALTAS' (Caspar, Melchior, Balthazar).

£1,500 - £2,000

FR-3634
Gold Epigraphic Ring
24mm

Inscribed in blackletter '+avemaria .sinelabe origin concep' (Hail Mary, conceived without sin) and internally 'ihs: ora pro mei e memento mei:' (Jesus pray for me and remember me).

£1,000 - £1,500

FR-2405
Gold
Inscribed
Ring
25mm
Inset garnet
cabochon
'+amor vin/
citomnia' 'love
conquers all'
in Lombardic
script.
From £2,000

FR-2714
Gold Inscribed
Ring
24mm
With cabochon
stone and 'MON
DIE U CESI'
(my God ...)
inscription.
£1,500 - £2,000

FR-249
Gold Inscribed
Ring
21mm
Engraved with
letters and
symbols (probably
of magical
significance), inset
sapphire cloison.
£1,000 - £1,500

FR-39112
Gold Inscribed Ring
18mm
Fronds and blackletter text 'en an bun' ('a good year').
From £800

FR-28426
Gold Inscribed Ring
19mm
Inscribed PRVDENTIA ('wisdom').
£500 - £800

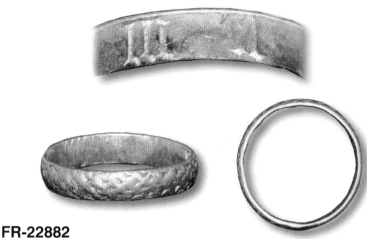

FR-22882
Gold Inscribed Ring
18mm
Marked 'eM' to the inner face.
£300 - £400

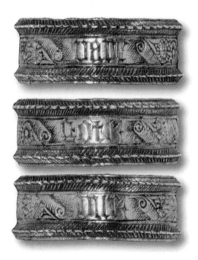

FR-9008
Gold Epigraphic Ring
21mm
Blackletter 'vane goteune', 'one [cheek] in vain'(?); Italian workmanship.
From £2,000

FR-32627
Gold Inscribed Stirrup
Ring
22mm
Inset turquoise; legend
in Lombardic script
'+DEV: DOINST: IOIE:
DEMAMOR: (God gives
me the joy of love).
From £1,000

FR-14672
Gold Inscribed Rosary
Ring
21mm
Thirteen scallops
with inscribed
+A+G+L+AGESVS
(magical text and 'Jesus').
£800 - £1,200

FR-47295
Gold Clasped Hands Ring
23mm
Two hands holding flowers
flanking a heart.
From £500

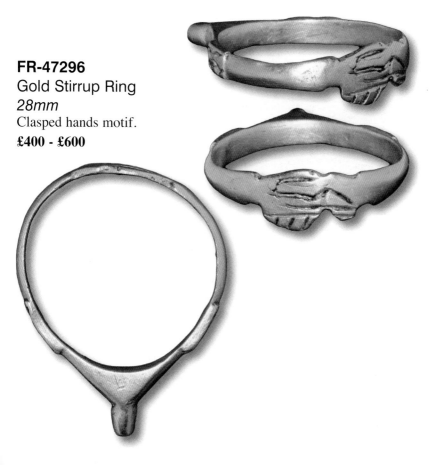

FR-47296
Gold Stirrup Ring
28mm
Clasped hands motif.
£400 - £600

SR-3761
Gold Inscribed Seal Ring
28mm
Engraved cross and m, n, h, a
on the ends of the arms.
From £2,000

FR-3741
Gold Stirrup Ring
27mm
Inset rectangular sapphire
cabochon.
From £800

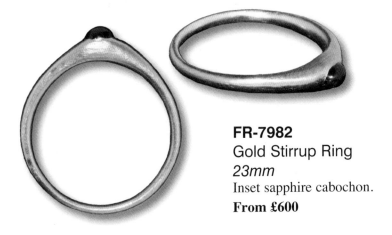

FR-7982
Gold Stirrup Ring
23mm
Inset sapphire cabochon.
From £600

FR-20353
Gold Stirrup Ring
22mm
Inset sapphire cabochon.
From £600

FR-18369
Gold Stirrup Ring
24mm
Inset sapphire cabochon.
From £600

FR-38457
Gold Stirrup Ring
23mm
Inset sapphire cabochon.
£500 - £800

FR-47294
Gold Stirrup Ring
26mm
Inset sapphire cabochon.
From £500

FR-4182
Gold Stirrup Ring
25mm
Triangular sapphire
cabochon.
From £600

FR-2328
Gold Stirrup Ring
25mm
Inset sapphire cabochon.
From £600

FR-1229
Gold Stirrup Ring
26mm
Inset sapphire cabochon.
From £600

FR-18837
Gold Stirrup Ring
22mm
Inset garnet cabochon.
£500 - £800

FR-45612
Gold Stirrup Ring
22mm
Inset ruby cabochon.
From £500

FR-19271
Gold Stirrup Ring
29mm
Inset amethyst cabochon.
From £1,500

FR-16106
Gold Stirrup Ring
24mm
Inset facetted amethyst.
From £800

FR-16409
Gold Stirrup Ring
27mm
Inset amethyst cabochon.
From £600

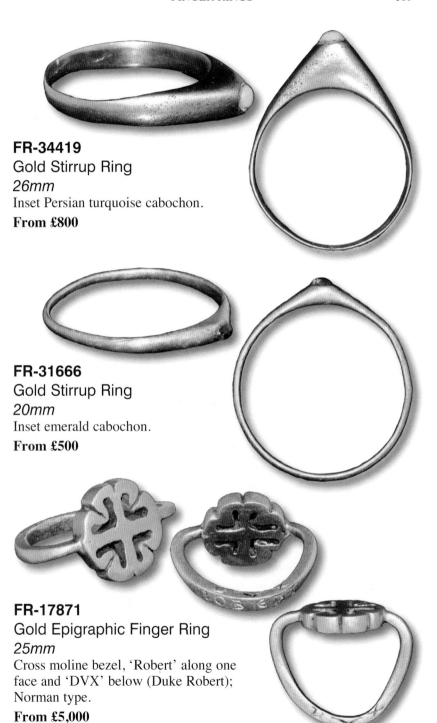

FR-34419
Gold Stirrup Ring
26mm
Inset Persian turquoise cabochon.
From £800

FR-31666
Gold Stirrup Ring
20mm
Inset emerald cabochon.
From £500

FR-17871
Gold Epigraphic Finger Ring
25mm
Cross moline bezel, 'Robert' along one
face and 'DVX' below (Duke Robert);
Norman type.
From £5,000

FR-22877
Gold Ring
22mm
Intaglio patriarchal
cross with star and
crescent moon.
£300 - £500

FR-2020
Gold Amuletic
Intaglio Ring
29mm
Inset garnet cabochon,
pseudo-alphabetic
inscription.
£300 - £500

FR-14613
Gold Lock Ring
23mm
'Fidelity in Love'
symbolism of the lock.
From £2,000

FR-2988
Gold Ring
21mm
St Catherine
motif.
From £2,000

FR-47339
Gold Iconographic
Ring
19mm
Corpus Christi motif.
From £1,000

FR-6763
Gold Ring
18mm
Interlocking hearts motif
£800 - £1,200

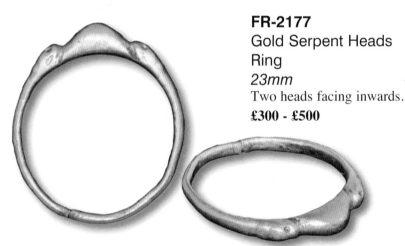

FR-2177
Gold Serpent Heads
Ring
23mm
Two heads facing inwards.
£300 - £500

FR-40617
Gold Entwined Snakes
Ring
23mm
Snake's head inserted
through a loop formed by a
second snake biting its own
tail.
£150 - £200

FR-26705
Gold Ring
19mm
Twisted wreath design.
£300 - £400

FR-1445
Gold Decorated Ring
23mm
Quatrefoil bezel engraved
with scrolls.
£800 - £1,200

FR-30376
Gold Decorated Ring
23mm
Bands of punched pellets
forming a continuous line.
£300 - £500

FR-35543
Gold Decorated Ring
19mm
Saltires, pellets and quatrefoils to the outer face.
£200 - £300

FR-1894
Gold Engraved Ring
18mm
Dot and billet punchmarks in three rows.
£200 - £300

FR-43733
Gold Ring
22mm
Inset octahedral diamond.
From £1,000

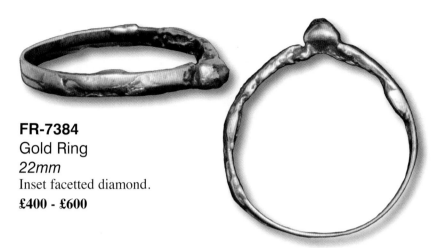

FR-7384
Gold Ring
22mm
Inset facetted diamond.
£400 - £600

FR-42177
Gold Ring
25mm
Inset rock crystal cabochon.
£500 - £800

FR-15737
Gold Ring
25mm
Inset conical facetted crystal.
£500 - £800

FR-19274
Gold Ring
24mm
Inset glass cabochon.
£200 - £300

FR-2121
Gold Ring
25mm
Inset Roman sapphire intaglio
with bust of Constantius I
(AD 250-306).
From £5,000

FR-19702
Gold Ring
24mm
Sapphire and four
emeralds.
From £2,000

FR-3738
Gold Ring
24mm
Inset carnelian and sapphire
cabochons.
From £1,500

FR-43830
Gold Ring
26mm
Inset sapphire cabochon.
From £2,000

FR-21026
Gold Stirrup Ring
22mm
Inset sapphire cabochon.
£800 - £1,200

FR-16460
Gold Ring
24mm
Inset sapphire cabochon.
From £800

FR-2342
Gold Ring
23mm
Inset sapphire
cabochon.
£600 - £900

FR-44864
Gold Ring
19mm
Inset sapphire cabochon.
£500 - £800

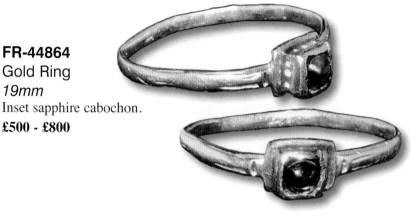

FR-8007
Gold Ring
23mm
Inset sapphire cabochon.
£500 - £800

FR-37988
Gold Ring
23mm
Inset sapphire cabochon.
£300 - £500

FR-43419
Gold Glove Ring with
Garnet
31mm
Inset garnet cabochon.
From £1,000

FR-3317
Gold Ring
28mm
Inset D-shaped garnet
cabochon.
£1,200 - £1,800

FR-5952
Gold and Garnet Ring
25mm
Elliptical bezel, central
garnet cabochon.
From £1,000

FR-44435
Gold Ring
22mm
Inset garnet cabochon.
£800 - £1,200

FR-1791
Gold Ring
23mm
Inset garnet cabochon.
£800 - £1,200

FR-15659
Gold Ring
27mm
Inset garnet cabochon.
£800 - £1,200

FR-14840
Gold Ring
25mm
Inset garnet
cabochon.
£800 - £1,200

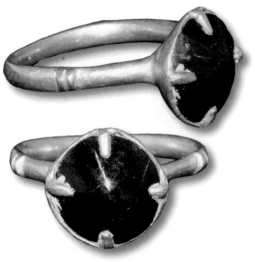

FR-16994
Gold Finger Ring
26mm
Conical garnet in a
claw setting.
£800 - £1,200

FR-2722
Gold Ring
24mm
Inset garnet
cabochon.
£500 - £800

FR-46509
Gold Ring
21mm
Inset garnet cabochon.
£500 - £800

FR-12904
Gold Ring
22mm
Inset cabochon garnet.
From £500

FR-2474
Gold Ring
19mm
Inset garnet cabochon.
£300 - £500

FR-2371
Gold Ring
19mm
Inset garnet cabochon.
£300 - £500

FR-3751
Gold Ring
19mm
Inset garnet cloison.
£200 - £300

FR-34384
Gold Ring with
Garnet
18mm
Inset conical garnet
cabochon.
£150 - £200

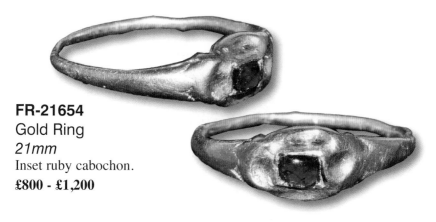

FR-21654
Gold Ring
21mm
Inset ruby cabochon.
£800 - £1,200

FR-7395
Gold Ring
22mm
Inset ruby cabochon.
£800 - £1,200

FR-2240
Gold Ring
26mm
Inset ruby cabochon
From £1,200

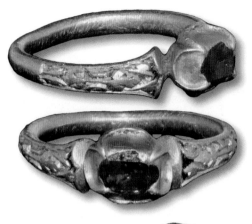

FR-15754
Gold Ring
23mm
Inset facetted ruby.
From £2,000

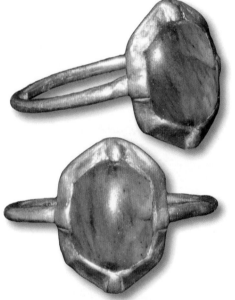

FR-19273
Gold Ring
23mm
Inset moss agate
cabochon.
£600 - £900

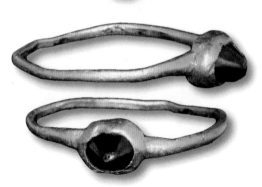

FR-4825
Gold Ring
21mm
Inset conical garnet.
£600 - £900

FR-42175
Gold Ring
23mm
Inset amethyst cabochon.
From £1,200

FR-7716
Gold Ring
24mm
Inset amethyst cabochon.
£800 - £1,200

FR-2687
Gold Ring
24mm
Inset amethyst cabochon.
£800 - £1,200

FR-3460
Gold Ring
26mm
Inset amethyst cabochon.
£800 - £1,200

FR-30027
Gold Ring
26mm
Inset pyramidal amethyst.
From £800

FR-42178
Gold Decorated Ring
19mm
Inset crescentic amethyst.
£500 - £800

FR-31936
Gold Ring
28mm
Inset blue-purple
irregular gemstone.
From £2,000

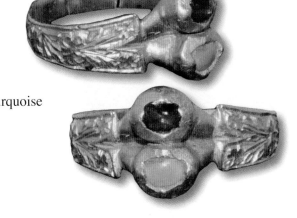

FR-8736
Gold Ring
16mm
With amethyst and turquoise
cabochons.
£400 - £600

FR-35916
Gold Ring
19mm
Inset turquoise cabochon.
£500 - £800

FR-879
Gold Ring
20mm
Inset turquoise cabochon.
£400 - £600

FR-2479
Gold Ring
19mm
Inset turquoise cabochon.
£400 - £600

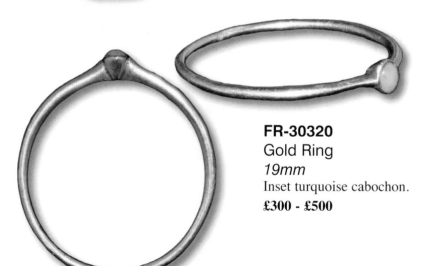

FR-30320
Gold Ring
19mm
Inset turquoise cabochon.
£300 - £500

FR-25547
Gold Ring
20mm
Inset turquoise cabochon;
Tudor type.
£100 - £200

FR-19272
Gold Ring
24mm
Inset blue glass cabochon;
Norman type.
£800 - £1,200

FR-37901
Gold Ring
25mm
Inset blue glass cabochon.
£400 - £600

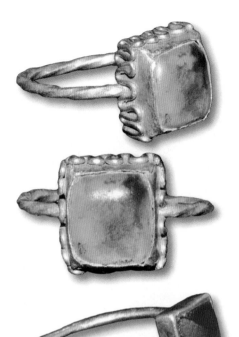

FR-21022
Gold Ring
24mm
Inset blue hardstone
cabochon.
£500 - £800

FR-38527
Gold Ring with Blue
Glass Setting
27mm
Rectangular cell bezel,
inset blue glass pyramid.
£300 - £500

FR-42176
Gold Ring
20mm
Inset jet cabochon.
£300 - £500

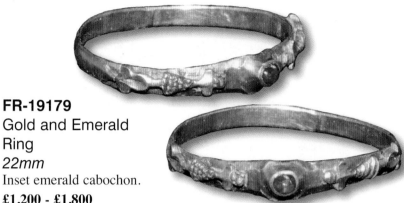

FR-19179
Gold and Emerald
Ring
22mm
Inset emerald cabochon.
£1,200 - £1,800

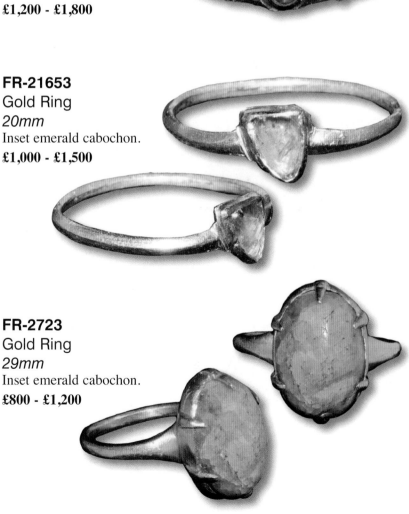

FR-21653
Gold Ring
20mm
Inset emerald cabochon.
£1,000 - £1,500

FR-2723
Gold Ring
29mm
Inset emerald cabochon.
£800 - £1,200

FR-16347
Gold Ring
24mm
Inset emerald cloison.
£500 - £800

FR-22778
Gold Ring
38mm
Two dolphins with conical
green stone cabochon.
From £2,000

FR-30319
Gold Ring
20mm
Pie-dish bezel, inset emerald
cabochon.
£300 - £500

FR-8587
Gold Ring
22mm
Inset green glass cloison.
£300 - £500

FR-3740
Gold Ring
22mm
Inset green glass cabochon.
£200 - £300

FR-2686
Gold Ring
23mm
Inset emerald cabochon.
£400 - £600

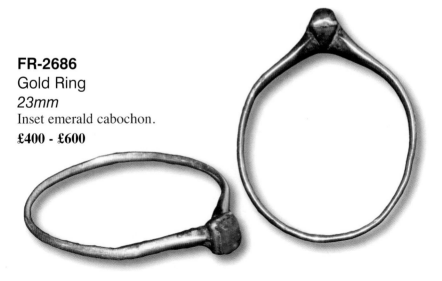

FR-2621
Gold Ring
20mm
Inset green glass cloison.
£300 - £500

FR-37900
Gold Ring
25mm
Inset peridot cabochon.
£400 - £600

FR-8580
Gold Seal Ring
22mm
Inscribed for Geoffrey
Rudel de Blaye.
From £2,000

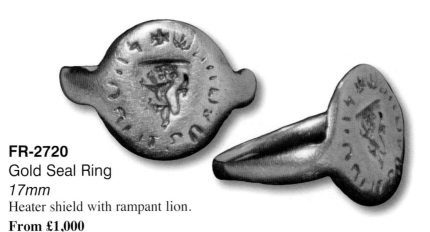

FR-2720
Gold Seal Ring
17mm
Heater shield with rampant lion.
From £1,000

FR-3610
Gold Inscribed Seal
Ring
22mm
Intaglio 'h' in blackletter script.
£300 - £500

FR-44433
Gold Jewish Signet Ring
23mm
Two fish and Hebrew inscription
'mordechai abraham bar [.]',
personal seal ring of 'Mordechai
Abraham the son of [?]'.
From £2,000

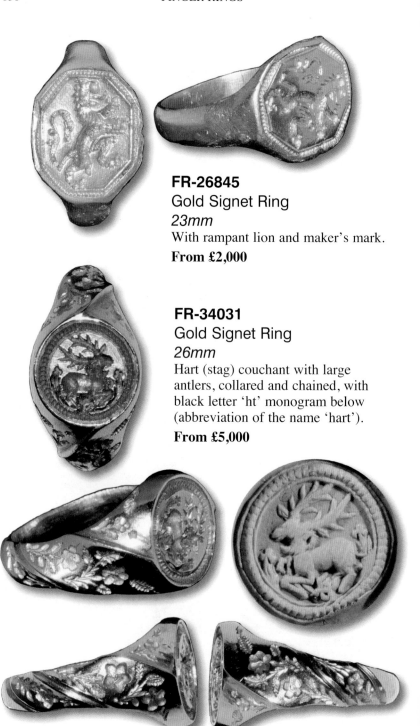

FR-26845
Gold Signet Ring
23mm
With rampant lion and maker's mark.
From £2,000

FR-34031
Gold Signet Ring
26mm
Hart (stag) couchant with large antlers, collared and chained, with black letter 'ht' monogram below (abbreviation of the name 'hart').
From £5,000

FR-45840
Gold Signet Ring
23mm
Reserved lion on a red enamel field.
£600 - £900

FR-52850
Gold Iconographic Ring
24mm
Panels with an angel, God the Father holding the infant Christ and the
Virgin Mary, 'I AM LOYAL' in black letter script.
From £5,000

FR-50506
Gold Cabochon Ring
22mm
Pie-dish bezel, inset garnet
cabochon.
From £800

FR-47484
Gold Clasped-Hands
Ring
27mm
Two hands supporting a
bowl, claw setting for a
conical amethyst.
From £2,000

FR-53328
Medieval Gold Ring
with Amethyst
19mm
Ovoid cell with inset
cabochon amethyst.
£400 - £600

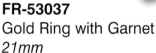

FR-53037
Gold Ring with Garnet
21mm
Openwork circle pattern with chevron border,
gold wire flower and garnet.
From £800

FR-48139
Gold Ring with Garnet
26mm
Pie-dish bezel, inset garnet
cabochon
From £600

FR-51599
Gold Ring with Facetted
Garnet
20mm
Crimped bezel, inset
rectangular garnet cloison.
£300 - £400

FR-50717
Gold Ring with Glass Cabochon
25mm
Octagonal plaque and facetted cone with inset glass cabochon.
From £800

FR-53035
Gold Ring with Glass Cabochon
20mm
Cupped bezel and polished glass cabochon.
£300 - £400

FR-48768
Gold Ribbed Ring
17mm
Hoop with beaded profile.
£150 - £200

FR-49828
Iconographic Saints Ring
15mm
Silver-gilt with flower sprays and sunbursts, standing figure with church tower and preaching cross.

From £300

FR-48072
Clasped Hands Ring
22mm
Silver-gilt hoop with clasped hands in low relief, transverse ribbed cuffs.

From £150

FR-52365
Silver Triple Cross Bezel Ring
23mm
Two voided saltires above the shoulders.

From £150

FR-51792
Gilt Ring with Beast
30mm
Faux-twist detailing, intaglio standing dog or wolf.
£150 - £200

FR-50057
Silver Ring with Niello Ornament
21mm
Niello panels with reserved saltire crosslets.
£100 - £150

FR-47088
Enamelled Ring
22mm
Enamelled floral and linear motifs.
£50 - £80

FR-47089
Pentagram Ring
21mm
Starburst on each shoulder,
incised pentagram and pellets.
£30 - £40

FR-44869
Gold Twisted Wreath Ring
19mm
Alternating plain and textured
panels imitating a wreath.
£400 - £600

FR-43734
Gilt Iconographic Ring
26mm
Silver-gilt fluted plaque with opposed saints.
From £200

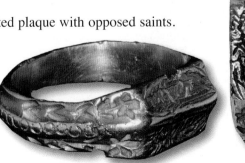

FR-43258
Gilt Iconographic Ring
24mm
Silver-gilt fluted plaque with St. John the Evangelist.
From £200

FR-42832
Gilt Iconographic Ring
20mm
Madonna and Child motif.
£120 - £180

FR-42796
Silver Ring
23mm
Beast-heads on the shoulders; Norman type.
£100 - £150

FR-45597
Silver Ring
30mm
Inlaid spirals, trumpet bezel with intaglio
standing bird.
£120 - £180

FR-45596
Silver Ring
27mm
Parcel-gilt and niello-inlaid
fleur-de-lys .
£200 - £300

FR-43792
Silver Ring with Intaglio
26mm
Inset blue enamel plaque with quadruped.
£40 - £60

FR-43328
Signet Ring with Monogram
28mm
Silver-gilt, intaglio blackletter minuscule monogram.
From £300

FR-43740
Decorated Ring
25mm
Pie-dish bezel with pyramid knop.
£100 - £150

FR-43790
Merchant's Signet Ring
32mm
Intaglio letter 'a' with fronds and stars.
£80 - £120

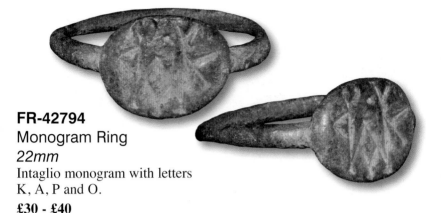

FR-42794
Monogram Ring
22mm
Intaglio monogram with letters
K, A, P and O.

£30 - £40

FR-46462
Quatrefoil Ring
21mm
Intaglio quatrefoil with pellets and
tendrils.

£30 - £40

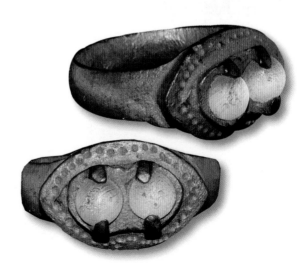

FR-45787
Amulet Ring
27mm
Plaque with two
crystal cabochons.

£40 - £60

FR-2480
Silver Inscribed Posy Ring
20mm
Inscribed 'aid a ben' (help for the good) in blackletter script.
£200 - £300

FR-16471
Silver-Gilt Inscribed Ring
26mm
Reserved text '+IESVSNZ' (Jesus of Nazareth).
£600 - £800

FR-2475
Silver Inscribed Ring
19mm
Engraved '+HO:ER[.] NCITOMNIA.[ ]' external inscription (bungled amorvincitomnia? 'love conquers all').
£200 - £300

FR-42184
Silver-Gilt Inscribed
Wedding Ring
21mm
Two figures holding hands,
Lombardic legend '+PER
TINVNCI' (for thee alone).
£200 - £300

FR-12619
Silver Inscribed Ring
26mm
Inscription to the inner face
'MAter dei memAnto' (for 'O
Mater Dei, memento mei' O
mother of God, remember me).
£150 - £200

FR-37904
Silver-Gilt Ring with
Inscribed Device
22mm
Incised triangular motif with
hatching.
£120 - £180

FR-11298
Silver Inscribed Ring
20mm
Pelletted cross and other
motifs.
£100 - £150

FR-2740
Silver Inscribed Ring
22mm
Capital 'R' motif.
£100 - £150

FR-11299
Silver Inscribed Ring
22mm
Incised blackletter 'b'
with foliage.
£100 - £150

FR-23756
Silver Epigraphic Ring
24mm

Fleur-de-lys motif with band reading '+S'IOHANISP' in Lombardic script for sigillum Iohannis P. (seal of John P.).

£100 - £150

FR-2210
Silver Clasped Hands Posy Ring
21mm

Engraved in Lombardic script 'moncoeurest a vous' (my heart is yours) between starbursts.

£200 - £300

FR-4049
Silver Inscribed Ring
22mm
Clasped hands motif
on the bezel; 'amore'
(love) and 'gorefe' (?) in
blackletter script.
£150 - £200

FR-2984
Silver Ring
21mm
Two clasped hands
modelled in the round.
£200 - £300

FR-47396
Silver Ring
23mm
Clasped hands motif.
£150 - £200

FR-4147
Silver Ring
19mm
Clasped hands motif.
£100 - £150

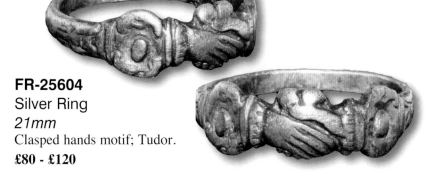

FR-25604
Silver Ring
21mm
Clasped hands motif; Tudor.
£80 - £120

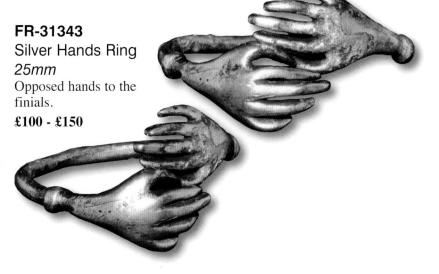

FR-31343
Silver Hands Ring
25mm
Opposed hands to the finials.
£100 - £150

FR-29074
Silver Ring
21mm
Clasped hands motif.
£80 - £120

FR-7682
Silver Stirrup Ring
19mm
Clasped hands motif, Latin
motto 'memento praeterit
et future temporis stet'
(remember the past and that
there is a future).
£300 - £500

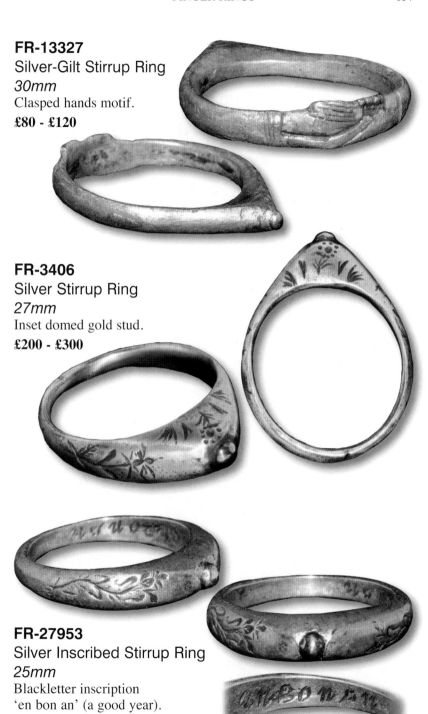

FR-13327
Silver-Gilt Stirrup Ring
30mm
Clasped hands motif.
£80 - £120

FR-3406
Silver Stirrup Ring
27mm
Inset domed gold stud.
£200 - £300

FR-27953
Silver Inscribed Stirrup Ring
25mm
Blackletter inscription
'en bon an' (a good year).
£150 - £200

FR-32244
Silver-Gilt
Iconographic
Ring
23mm
Images of plants
below St Barbara
with a branch and
St Catherine with
a wheel above her
shoulder.
From £200

FR-15486
Silver-Gilt
Iconographic
Type Ring
24mm
Chevrons and
hatching (no icon).
£300 - £400

FR-4989
Silver Iconographic
Ring
22mm
Motif of two saints.
£100 - £150

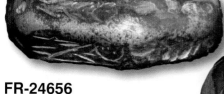

FR-24656
Silver Iconographic Ring
20mm
Images of saints partially
remaining; Norman type.
£80 - £120

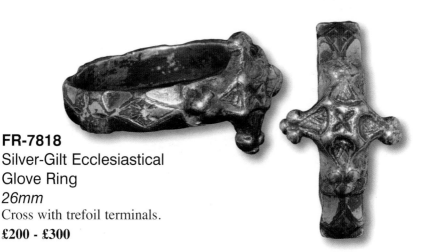

FR-7818
Silver-Gilt Ecclesiastical
Glove Ring
26mm
Cross with trefoil terminals.
£200 - £300

FR-21043
Silver Reliquary
Ring
23mm
Incised starburst
design; inset bone
relic fragment to the
underside.
£100 - £150

FR-4682
Silver Ring
21mm
Cross of Lorraine
motif.
£100 - £150

FR-45986
Silver-Gilt Ring with
Falconry Scene
27mm
Bird of prey seizing a
smaller bird motif.
£150 - £200

FR-4386
Silver Teutonic Eagle Ring
20mm
Engraved eagle with extended
wings.
£100 - £150

FR-40653
Silver Ring
24mm
Scrolled border with intaglio
agnus dei.
£150 - £200

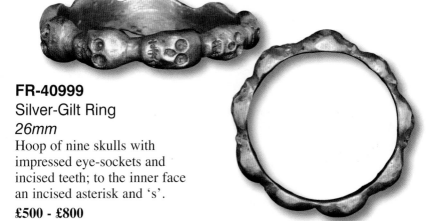

FR-40999
Silver-Gilt Ring
26mm
Hoop of nine skulls with
impressed eye-sockets and
incised teeth; to the inner face
an incised asterisk and 's'.
£500 - £800

FR-33932
Silver Heart Ring
19mm
Incised heart with fleur-de-lys and dashes in the field.
£80 - £120

FR-33931
Silver-Gilt Ring
26mm
Four fronds and lozenge.
£100 - £150

FR-23463
Silver Quatrefoil Ring
21mm
Intaglio quatrefoil motif.
£100 - £150

FR-33240
Silver Decorated Ring
21mm
Intaglio capital 'A', hatched uprights and
trefoil serifs.
£80 - £120

FR-18473
Silver Decorated
Ring
23mm
Niello-inlaid scrolls.
£80 - £120

FR-26086
Silver Decorated Ring
20mm
Stook of corn motif.
£100 - £150

FR-518
Silver-Gilt Decorated
Ring
22mm
Incised zigzag pattern.
£80 - £120

FR-31316
Silver-Gilt Teardrop Ring
24mm
Teardrop bezel with vesica
motif.
£100 - £150

FR-6156
Silver-Gilt Decorated
Ring
21mm
Star-in-lozenge motifs.
£150 - £200

FR-351
Silver-Gilt Decorated
Ring
23mm
Incised and punched diamond
pattern.
£80 - £120

FR-2574
Silver
Enamelled
Ring
28mm
Gilt panel with
cross and enamel
infill.
£100 - £150

FR-3249
Silver Ring
25mm
Winged angels
motif.
£300 - £500

FR-3615
Silver
Monogram
Ring
20mm
Engraved foliage
and monogram.
£80 - £120

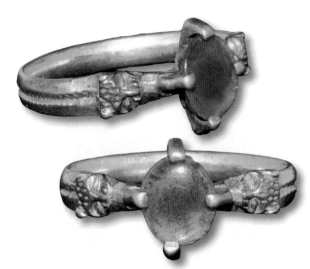

FR-42183
Silver-Gilt
Doublet Ring
23mm
Inset crystal
cabochon in
talon setting.
£150 - £200

FR-15635
Silver Ring
29mm
Inset crystal cabochon.
£100 - £150

FR-26084
Silver-Gilt Decorated
Ring
25mm
Inset red glass cabochon.
£80 - £120

FR-7302
Silver Intaglio Ring
25mm
Inset red gemstone cabochon.
£100 - £150

FR-32584
Silver Ring
26mm
Inset red hardstone
cloison.
£100 - £150

FR-34017
Silver-Gilt Ring
23mm
Inset rectangular
facetted garnet.
£400 - £600

FR-33244
Silver-Gilt
Decorated Ring
26mm
Inset emerald
cabochon.
£100 - £150

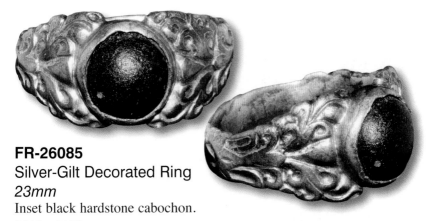

FR-26085
Silver-Gilt Decorated Ring
23mm
Inset black hardstone cabochon.
£100 - £150

FR-33238
Silver Seal Matrix Ring
24mm
Intaglio heater shield with three flowers, hook motifs above.
£100 - £150

FR-31811
Silver Seal Matrix Ring
26mm
Lombardic capital 'I' with hatched uprights and frond.
£100 - £150

FR-26093
Silver Seal Matrix Ring
22mm
Intaglio fleur-de-lys motif.
£100 - £150

FR-20311
Silver Seal Matrix Ring
23mm
Engraved saltire.
£100 - £150

FR-18451
Silver Seal Matrix Ring
27mm
Intaglio lion motif.
£100 - £150

FR-23978
Silver-Gilt Seal Matrix Ring
22mm
Intaglio double-headed eagle and Cyrillic text.
£120 - £180

FR-33230
Silver-Gilt Seal Matrix
Ring
24mm
Hatched capital 'I' with
star and crescents.
£100 - £150

FR-26694
Silver-Gilt Seal Matrix Ring
24mm
Leaf with scrolls and stalks.
£100 - £150

FR-26094
Silver-Gilt Seal Matrix
Ring
26mm
Intaglio fleur-de-lys motif.
£100 - £150

FR-33229
Silver-Gilt Seal Ring
29mm
Fleur-de-lys motif.
£100 - £150

FR-23979
Silver-Gilt Seal Matrix
Ring
24mm
Intaglio running animal
motif, stars and punched
point border.
£100 - £150

FR-4681
Silver Inscribed Seal Ring
21mm
Bird motif and enigmatic text '+s*neom[.]'.
£150 - £200

FR-21093
Silver Seal Ring
22mm
'Pelican in her piety' motif and legend '+voimovaid'.
£100 - £150

FR-16988
Silver Seal Ring
30mm
Griffin motif.
£150 - £200

FR-11297
Silver Seal Ring
20mm
Two standing robed figures
and '+avemaria:' (Hail
Mary).
£100 - £150

FR-16306
Silver-Gilt Seal Ring
23mm
Agnus Dei motif.
£200 - £300

FR-15047
Silver-Gilt Signet Ring
21mm
Engraved wreath and stag's
head crest.
£200 - £300

FR-28017
Silver-Gilt Signet Ring
31mm
Regardant lion with raised tail.
£120 - £180

FR-25987
Silver Signet Ring
21mm
Intaglio bull's head with
band of symbols.
£80 - £120

FR-37927
Inscribed Ring
23mm
Intaglio capital 'R'.
£80 - £120

FR-9547
Epigraphic Magic Ring
21mm
Incised magical sigils.
£80 - £120

FR-46463
Engraved Ring
22mm
Bronze hoop with starburst
and incised pentagram.
£40 - £60

FR-47089
Engraved Ring
21mm
Bronze hoop with pentagram
and pellets.
£50 - £80

FR-14979
Engraved Ring
22mm
Pentagram motif.
£50 - £80

FR-42185
Ring with Bust
23mm
Beaded border, profile
African bust.
£80 - £120

FR-26242
Figural Ring
23mm
Intaglio centaur with
round shield and raised
sword; Norman type.
£80 - £120

FR-42038
Figural Ring
24mm
Intaglio warrior with raised
shield.
£80 - £120

FR-38144
Engraved Ring
20mm
Bird motifs to the shoulders,
intaglio dove with olive
branch in its beak.
£80 - £120

FR-27601
Engraved Ring
25mm
With horned devil motif.
£100 - £150

FR-2946
Engraved Ring
24mm
Inlaid silver cross botonny; Crusader
type.
£80 - £120

FR-3652
Elliptical Ring
24mm
Carinated shoulders.
£20 - £30

FR-33233
Seal Matrix Ring
24mm
Intaglio hippocampus and beaded
border.
£50 - £80

FR-18870
Seal Matrix Ring
22mm
Intaglio agnus dei and legend
'+MARTINVS' (Martin) in
Lombardic script.
£50 - £80

FR-33231
Seal Matrix Ring
26mm
Intaglio capital 'L' with
hatched upright.
£50 - £80

FR-33058
Seal Matrix Ring
26mm
Intaglio blackletter 'n' with
cross behind.
£50 - £80

FR-17332
Seal Matrix Ring
27mm
Intaglio Lombardic capital
'R' with pellets and leaf.
£50 - £80

FR-42035
Seal Ring
28mm
Intaglio running horse.
£80 - £120

FR-19590
Seal Ring
20mm
Spread-eagle motif and text
'SIGILVMSA[..]' (seal of Sa[..]).
£50 - £80

FR-25989
Personal Seal Ring
23mm
Intaglio bull's head
with star between the
horns, wreath below,
'+INVDIRTNVDIRTNV'
inscription.
£120 - £180

FR-74
Signet Ring
29mm
Incised standing figure of a
king holding sceptre and orb.
£50 - £80

FR-39595
Signet Ring
25mm
Intaglio 'W' surmounted by a
crown within a cartouche.
£40 - £60

FR-T0105
Signet Ring
23mm
With initials 'BW' in a border; Tudor.
£30 - £50

AR-46583
Gold Archer's Ring
40mm
Scrolled ornament.
From £800

AR-2741
Silver Archer's Ring
23mm
Geometric ornament and
central foliate motif.
£80 - £120

AR-4188
Silver Archer's Ring
21mm
Hatching with three-band
ropework border.
£120 - £180

AR-31124
Silver Archer's Ring
39mm
Ropework ornament with
zigzag and scroll.
£120 - £180

AR-42114
Silver Child's Archer's Ring
26mm
Scrolled ornament.
£50 - £80

AR-40288
Child's Archer's Ring
24mm
Geometric ornament.
£80 - £120

AR-3631
Archer's Ring
28mm
Geometric ornament on hatched background.
£50 - £80

AR-4679
Archer's Ring
36mm
Geometric ornament.
£50 - £80

AR-9265
Archer's Ring
41mm
Foliate ornament, central leaf.
£80 - £120

AR-18066
Archer's Ring
37mm
Scrolled ornament.
£50 - £80

AR-26585
Archer's Ring
36mm
Foliate ornament and chevrons.
£80 - £120

AR-33948
Archer's Ring
34mm
Hatching and
herringbone panels.
£50 - £80

AR-33949
Archer's Ring
31mm
Hatched panels.
£50 - £80

AR-40654
Archer's Ring
43mm
Scrolled foliage panels.
£50 - £80

FR-50062
Bone Archer's Ring
27mm
Flange with incised lines
and points.
£80 - £120

FR-44955
Archer's Ring
43mm
Flange with lateral bulbs.
£50 - £80

FR-44956
Archer's Ring
39mm
Ropework and scrolled
patterns.
£50 - £80

We are accepting single entries and collections of coins and antiquities

Secondary Phase - Series H Type 49 Variety Ib
Woden Head Sceatta

Central London
Auction Venue

TimeLine Auctions Limited
The Court House
363 Main Road
Harwich, Essex
CO12 4DN

www.timelineauctions.com

+44 [0]1277 815121
enquiries@timelineauctions.com

HARNESS PENDANTS AND FITTINGS

Harness pendants were used for decorative and practical purposes in the medieval period. They formed part of the standard equipment for a horse belonging to a man of wealth, a nobleman or a churchman and for members of their retinues. Considerable care was taken to provide an attractive and artistic embellishment to the harness straps and fittings. On a more practical level, the heraldic types of pendant served as badges of identification and ownership. Pendants without heraldic motifs were probably used for their decorative value.

Bannerets were rectangular bronze panels with a tube to one long edge and enamelled heraldic motifs to both faces, designed to be seen from both sides. They were attached to horse harness by a rod passing through the tube, projecting from a baseplate. Some examples show the same arms on both faces, while others show them reversed, i.e. a lion facing left on one face is shown facing right on the other. It is often possible to determine the owner's family from the heraldry, and from the style of the pendant also an indication of the date. Royal pendants are not as rare as might be expected, because heralds and other officials could bear the royal arms on their equipment as a badge of office.

Mounts and studs with heraldic and religious motifs were a popular means of personalising items for reasons of prestige. Some were worn on belts and horse harness, as well as being attached to portable items.

Heraldic items such as pendants and bannerets are heavily collected for the information they provide concerning individual families, as well as for the beauty of their design and execution and their associations with historic figures.

HP-46060
Peacock
Horse Harness
Banneret
43mm
Reserved peacock
with foliage.
£200 - £300

HP-6346
'Sir Thomas de
Pin' Heraldic
Banneret
22mm
Chevron on a red
field between pine
cones.
£150 - £200

HP-18337
'John
L'Estrange'
Heraldic
Banneret
57mm
Red enamel with
two lions passant
gardant.
£500 - £800

HP-26758
'Applegh Family' Heraldic Banneret
44mm
Green enamelled scrolled foliage and red fruit, a white ape with a chain to its middle.
£300 - £500

HP-18338
Heraldic Banneret
44mm
White hart motif.
£300 - £500

HP-53325
Heraldic Lion Horse Harness Pendant
28mm
White enamelled lion rampant regardant.
£80 - £120

HP-47305
Heraldic 'de Bohun Family' Horse Harness Pendant
45mm
Blue enamel with reserved lions and double bar.
£80 - £120

HP-33397
Heraldic 'de Bohun Family' Horse Harness Pendant
36mm
Blue enamel with six reserved lions and double bar.
£80 - £120

HP-21564
Heraldic 'de Bohun Family' Horse Harness Pendant
36mm
Six lions rampant and a diagonal bar.
£80 - £120

HP-17253
Heraldic 'de Bohun Family' Horse Harness Pendant
38mm
Lozenge-shaped, blue enamel with reserved diagonal lines and six lions.
£80 - £120

HP-52865
Heraldic Leopard Horse Harness Pendant
39mm
Leopard surrounded by flowers and foliage.
£50 - £80

HP-53322
Heraldic 'Edward The Confessor' Horse Harness Pendant
43mm
Cross between five martlets on a blue enamel field.
£80 - £120

HP-47942
Heraldic 'Cossington Family' Horse Harness Pendant
45mm
Three reserved cinquefoils on a blue enamel field.
£80 - £120

HP-53323
Heraldic 'Ufford Family' Horse Harness Pendant
45mm
Reserved border and cross engrailed
£50 - £80

HP-48513
Heraldic 'Stag' Horse Harness Pendant
48mm
White enamelled stag with red antlers, head of a deer beneath the hooves.
£100 - £150

HP-40591
Heraldic 'Bishop of Ely' Horse Harness Pendant
39mm
Three reserved crowns.
£50 - £80

HP-48751
Heraldic 'Blücher Family' Horse Harness Pendant
41mm
Red enamel escutcheon with crossed keys; European type
£80 - £120

HP-48517
Heraldic Horse Harness Pendant
37mm
Chevron with a label overall (used by the eldest son during his father's lifetime).
£80 - £120

HP-52857
Heraldic Royal
Horse Harness
Pendant
39mm
Unusual disc form, three
lions of England on red
enamel field.
£80 - £120

HP-47504
'Sacred Heart'
Bifacial Horse
Harness Pendant
56mm
One face with crowned
heart, the other with
heater shield with
seven horizontal
bars, Lombardic text
'S CORD [.]SI[.]
SIENADUA (Sacred
Heart of ...); European
type.
From £200

HP-52861
Horse Harness Pendant
75mm
Cross with equal-armed cross inside, large
hanger with dog's head finials.
£50 - £80

HP-51326
Heraldic
'Unicorn'
Pendant
Hanger
25mm
Plaque with hinge
below, white
enamelled running
unicorn motif.
£40 - £60

HP-53324
Heraldic Horse
Harness Pendant
Group
38-43mm
Two heater-shaped and
one lozenge-shaped
pendants, each with
enamelled lion gardant and
three-branched tree in the
field.
£200 - £300

HP-52956
Heraldic 'Roald De Burgh' Harness Fitting
48mm
Enamelled swan with neck bent.
£50 - £80

HP-43423
Heraldic 'King Edward I' Horse Harness Pendant
41mm
Heater shield with red enamel fill, three gilt lions passant gardant.
£80 - £120

HP-44866
Heraldic 'Andrews Family' Horse Pendant
41mm
Silvered bronze, gold saltire on a blue enamel field, four crosses in the quarters
£50 - £80

HP-47307
Heraldic 'Gifford Family'
Horse Harness Pendant
27mm
Three reserved lions on a red
enamel field.
£50 - £80

HP-47306
Heraldic 'Ufford Family'
Horse Harness Pendant
36mm
Cross engrailed on a black
enamel field.
£30 - £40

HP-43418
Heraldic Bifacial Horse
Harness Pendant
43mm
Reserved dragon with raised
head and looped tail on both
faces.
£100 - £150

HP-46249
Heraldic Gilt Horse Harness Mount
37mm
Heater shield with gilded looped knot and trefoil finial.
£100 - £150

HP-45608
Heraldic Mermaid Horse Harness Pendant
34mm
Mermaid holding a flower in the left hand and fish in the right hand, Lombardic legend 'IESVIL [.]HEIREMI' (I am ...?)
£80 - £120

HP-45609
Heraldic Horse Harness Pendant
23mm
Heater shield with red enamel cross on a silver field, reserved legend 'AVE MARIA GRACIA' (Hail Mary [full of] grace) in Lombardic capitals on white enamel field.
£80 - £120

HP-44897
Heraldic Royal
Horse Harness
Pendant
30mm
Lion passant on a
blue enamel field,
fleurs-de-lys on red
enamel lobes.

£50 - £80

HP-44898
Heraldic Horse Harness Mount
31mm
Heater shield with punched-point design,
the chief with two saltires, chevron below.

£50 - £80

HP-44871
Heraldic Lion
Horse Harness
Pendant
33mm
Lion rampant with
raised tail.

£50 - £80

HP-44909
Heraldic Fleur-De-Lys Horse Harness Mount
36mm
Lozenge with recessed fleur-de-lys, lateral lobes and arms.
£50 - £80

HP-45782
Heraldic Horse Harness Mount
36mm
Quartered field with kneeling swordsman and lion rampant.
£30 - £40

HP-47304
Heraldic Unicorn Horse Harness Pendant
46mm
Heater-shield with enamelled white unicorn on a green field, rosette above.
£80 - £120

HP-53087
Gilt Horse Harness
Pendant Mount
30mm
Heraldic lion-mask.
£50 - £80

HP-16714
'Richard III' Heraldic Horse
Harness Pendant with Hanger
32mm
High-relief motifs of a boar's head, a
crescent and a star below.
From £500

HP-46061
Heraldic Butterfly
Horse Harness
Pendant
44mm
Gilt-bronze with
butterfly volant
on red
enamelled field.
£120 - £180

HP-15165
'Francois I of France' Heraldic Horse Harness Pendant
66mm
Reserved 'I', double-headed S-curved salamander on a red and blue enamel field.
From £200

HP-31655
'Baron de la Pole' Heraldic Silver Pendant
30mm
Quartered arms, one and four a bar between three leopards' heads, two and three a lion rampant.
From £2,000

HP-47307
'Sir John Gifford' Heraldic Horse Harness Pendant
27mm
Reserved three lions on a red enamel field.
£50 - £80

HP-26426
'Sir John Gifford'
Heraldic Horse
Harness Pendant
27mm
Red enamelled field with
gilt lions passant and a
blue three-bar label.
£50 - £80

HP-40597
'Spigurnell
Family' Heraldic
Horse Harness
Pendant
46mm
Reserved lion
passant on a field
of lozenges.
£80 - £120

HP-35720
'De Mowbray Family'
Heraldic Horse Harness
Pendant
42mm
Red enamelled field with
white lion rampant.
£80 - £120

HP-37202
'Duke of Normandy'
Heraldic Horse
Harness Pendant
42mm
Red enamelled shield
with two lions passant,
Norman type.
£120 - £180

HP-26745
'Chandos Family'
Heraldic Horse
Harness Pendant
55mm
Red enamelled lion;
with cruciform hanger.
£80 - £120

HP-21566
'De La Pole'
Heraldic
Horse Harness
Pendant
44mm
Lion rampant in red
enamel on a yellow
field.
£80 - £120

HP-35663
'Prince Edward II' Heraldic Horse
Harness Pendant
44mm
Red enamelled field with three gold
lions, blue label.
£80 - £120

HP-12288
'Royal Arms
of England'
Heraldic
Horse Harness
Pendant
35mm
Reserved three
lions passant
gardant on a red
enamel field.
£40 - £60

HP-43423
'Edward I' Horse
Harness Pendant
41mm
Reserved three gilt lions
passant gardant on red
enamel field.
£100 - £150

HP-40599
'Royal Arms of
England' Heraldic
Horse Harness
Pendant
48mm
Red enamel with three
reserved lions passant
gardant.
£40 - £60

HP-40598
'Royal Arms of England'
Heraldic Horse Harness
Pendant
33mm
Red enamel with three
reserved lions passant
gardant.
£100 - £150

HP-35706
'Royal Arms of England'
Heraldic Horse Harness
Pendant
48mm
Red enamel with three reserved
lions passant gardant.
£100 - £150

HP-21646
Differenced 'Royal Arms of
England' Heraldic Horse
Harness Pendant
31mm
Three lions passant gardant on a
red field with a blue enamel label.
£120 - £180

HP-19617
'Royal Arms of England' Heraldic Horse-Harness Pendant
30mm
Red enamel with three reserved lions passant gardant.
£80 - £120

HP-4851
'Royal Arms' Heraldic Horse-Harness Pendant
49mm
Royal arms of England and France, quartered.
£150 - £200

HP-32346
Heraldic Horse Harness Pendant
42mm
Reserved lion passant on a red enamelled field.
£30 - £50

HP-4933
Heraldic Horse Harness Pendant
67mm
Gilded, lion rampant beneath three
fleurs-de-lys.
£50 - £80

HP-38503
Heraldic Horse
Harness Pendant
36mm
Advancing lion with
raised tail.
£40 - £60

HP-26427
'Royal Arms of England'
Heraldic Horse Harness
Pendant
40mm
Lions passant and fleurs-de-lys.
£50 - £80

HP-40608
'Royal Arms of England'
Heraldic Horse Harness
Pendant
32mm
Red enamelled field with
reserved fleurs-de-lys and
lion passant gardant.
£40 - £60

HP-16835
'Royal Arms of England'
Heraldic Horse Harness
Pendant
44mm
Red enamel field with
three reserved lions passant
gardant.
£50 - £80

HP-16764
'Royal Arms of
England' Horse
Harness Pendant
42mm
Three gilded lions
passant gardant on a red
enamelled field.
£80 - £120

HP-3644
Horse Harness
Pendant
68mm
Regardant lion motif.
£150 - £200

HP-16499
Heraldic Horse
Harness Pendant
41mm
Red enamel with reserved
lion passant within a
border of trefoils.
£80 - £120

HP-40606
Heraldic Horse
Harness Pendant
27mm
Red enamelled field with
reserved lion passant,
four blue panels.
£40 - £60

HP-18356
Heraldic Horse
Harness Pendant
40mm
Blue enamel field
with two lions passant
gardant.
£100 - £150

HP-40595
Heraldic Horse
Harness Pendant
42mm
Reserved manticore
rampant.
£50 - £80

HP-40607
Heraldic Horse
Harness Pendant
40mm
Red enamelled field with
reserved fleur-de-lys and
griffin (or lion) passant.
£40 - £60

HP-40601
Heraldic Horse Harness Pendant
60mm
Blue enamel with reserved lion rampant.
£30 - £40

HP-40593
Heraldic Horse
Harness Pendant
53mm
White enamelled lion
rampant.
£40 - £60

HP-17254
'De Montacute Family' Quatrefoil Heraldic Horse Harness Pendant
45mm
Blue enamelled field with reserved griffin rampant.
£50 - £80

HP-40605
'Read Family' Heraldic Horse Harness Pendant
39mm
Blue enamelled field and reserved griffin.
£50 - £80

HP-40594
Heraldic Horse Harness Pendant
42mm
Red enamel field with white griffin.
£100 - £150

HP-9274
Heraldic Horse
Harness Pendant
39mm
Blue enamel field with
white griffin.
£50 - £80

HP-30040
Heraldic Horse
Harness Pendant
41mm
Red enamel with
reserved griffin.
£50 - £80

HP-17255
Heraldic Horse
Harness Pendant
38mm
Blue enamel field
with reserved dragon
passant.
£50 - £80

HP-40602
Heraldic Horse Harness
Pendant
54mm
Dragon in the field.
£50 - £80

HP-37916
Heraldic Horse Harness
Pendant
39mm
Enamelled leopard advancing
surrounded by foliage.
£80 - £120

HP-47304
Heraldic Horse
Harness Pendant
46mm
Enamelled white unicorn
on a green field with rosette
above.
£80 - £120

HP-40592
Heraldic Horse Harness Pendant
41mm
Red enamel field with reserved white
enamel unicorn passant.
£100 - £150

HP-42245
Heraldic Horse
Harness Pendant
52mm
Enamelled white
running horse, green
trefoils above and
below.
£100 - £150

HP-26425
Heraldic
Horse Harness
Pendant
25mm
Advancing bear
motif.
£80 - £120

HP-T0108
Heraldic
Horse Harness
Pendant
42mm
Eagle motif.
£300 - £500

HP-23089
'Monthermer Family'
Heraldic Horse Harness
Pendant
40mm
Gilt field with green enamel
eagle; to the reverse, pelletted
border and escutcheon with three
vertical bars.
£80 - £120

HP-26414
Heraldic Horse
Harness Pendant
Hanger
37mm
Horse with raised tail and
regardant head.
£100 - £150

HP-26748
'Chauncy Family'
Heraldic Horse Harness
Pendant
41mm
Red enamelled field with three
spread eagles.
£80 - £120

HP-17155
'De Lindsay Family'
Heraldic Horse Harness
Pendant
50mm
Blue enamelled field with
gold fleur-de-lys alternating
with red field and gold eagle.
£100 - £150

HP-26422
Heraldic Horse
Harness Pendant
26mm
Bird with extended
feet and tail, feather
detailing.
£80 - £120

HP-21642
Heraldic Horse
Harness Pendant
38mm
Addorsed birds executed
in white enamel.
£50 - £80

HP-23106
Heraldic
Horse Harness
Pendant
52mm
Advancing bird
with coiled neck,
Norman type.
£80 - £120

HP-21548
'Eton Family' Bifacial Heraldic
Horse Harness Pendant
40mm
To one face, red enamel field with
chevron and three eagles; to the
reverse, blue enamel field with
six fleurs-de-lys.
£150 - £200

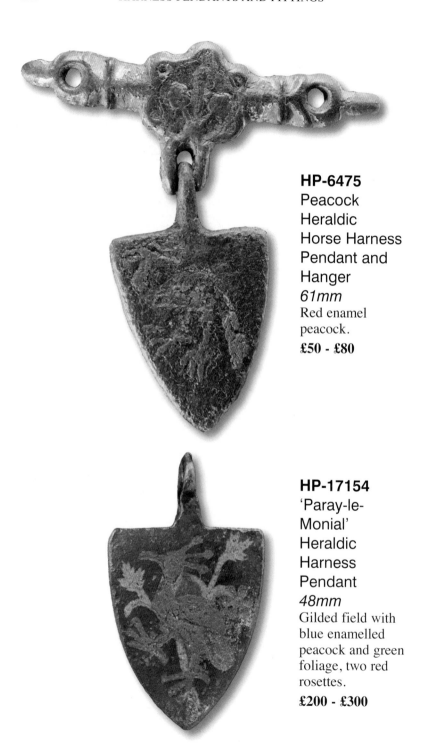

HP-6475
Peacock
Heraldic
Horse Harness
Pendant and
Hanger
61mm
Red enamel
peacock.
£50 - £80

HP-17154
'Paray-le-
Monial'
Heraldic
Harness
Pendant
48mm
Gilded field with
blue enamelled
peacock and green
foliage, two red
rosettes.
£200 - £300

HP-40591
'Bishop of Ely'
Heraldic Horse
Harness Pendant
39mm
Three reserved crowns.
£40 - £60

HP-40590
'Bishop of Ely'
Heraldic Horse
Harness Pendant
44mm
Three reserved crowns.
£80 - £120

HP-21546
'House of Lancaster'
Heraldic Harness
Pendant
64mm
Crown over 'S' in a gilded
border.
£150 - £200

HP-32347
'Sir Roger Trumpington' Heraldic Horse Harness Pendant
36mm
Two trumpets on a field of crosses.
£100 - £150

HP-34265
'Aubrey De Vere' Heraldic Horse Harness Pendant
37mm
Enamelled field quartered yellow and red with expanding-arm cross.
£80 - £120

HP-30049
'Beauchamp Family' Heraldic Horse Harness Pendant
42mm
Red enamel field with reserved crosses and a median bar.
£150 - £200

HP-30047
'Duchy of Bar'
Heraldic Horse
Harness Pendant
19mm
Blue enamel field with
reserved crosses and two
vertical pikes.
£50 - £80

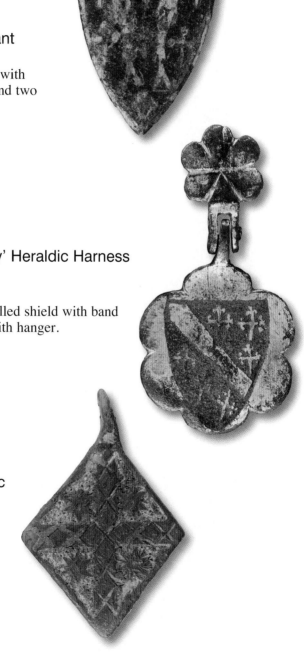

HP-26754
'Howard Family' Heraldic Harness
Pendant
62mm
Gilded, red enamelled shield with band
and six crosses; with hanger.
£500 - £800

HP-6504
'Ballantyne
Family' Heraldic
Harness
Pendant
45mm
Lozenge plaque,
cross and four
stars.
£100 - £150

HP-12282
'Peverell Family'
Heraldic Harness
Pendant
40mm
Chequered blue band, red
field with six lions.
£150 - £200

HP-17252
'Multon Family' Heraldic
Harness Pendant
39mm
Red enamel squares and a
blue cross.
£150 - £200

HP-6505
'Camden Family' Heraldic
Harness Pendant
44mm
Horizontal bar and six crosses
on a blue enamel field.
£150 - £200

HP-30031
'Ricard De La Rokele'
Heraldic Horse Harness
Pendant
39mm
Red enamel lozenges with
diagonal band.
£100 - £120

HP-40603
'De Quincy Family'
Heraldic Horse Harness
Pendant
40mm
Red enamel with reserved
cinquefoil.
£120 - £180

HP-40600
'De Clare Family' Heraldic
Horse Harness Pendant
32mm
Red enamel chevrons.
£80 - £120

HP-40596
'Sir Guy Botetourt'
Heraldic Horse
Harness Pendant
49mm
Saltire engrailed motif.
£80 - £120

HP-39111
'Sir Robert Fitzwalter'
Heraldic Horse
Harness Pendant
43mm
Red enamelled chevrons
and transverse bar.
£100 - £150

HP-35705
'Despenser Family'
Heraldic Horse
Harness Pendant
36mm
Red and black enamel
quarters.
£100 - £150

HP-32604
'De Warenne
Family' Heraldic
Horse Harness
Pendant
21mm
Enamelled chequer
pattern, gold and
blue.
£50 - £80

HP-32587
'Deincourt Family' Heraldic Horse
Harness Pendant
53mm
Reserved facing mask with red and blue
enamel field.
£100 - £150

HP-31694
'Earl of Derby'
Quatrefoil Heraldic
Horse Harness
Pendant
41mm
Heater shield on
a red enamelled
background.
£100 - £150

HP-21648
'Burgh Family' Heraldic
Horse Harness Pendant
43mm
Blue enamelled field with
three white fleurs-de-lys.
£200 - £300

HP-16088
'Sir Robert de Tibetot'
Heraldic Horse Harness
Pendant
54mm
Enamelled white field with
red saltire engrailed.
£120 - £180

HP-19615
'Henry de Pembridge'
Heraldic Horse Harness
Pendant
45mm
Six blue and white enamelled
stripes and a red band.
£80 - £120

HP-T0105
'Chamberlayne Family' Heraldic Horse
Harness Pendant
65mm
Hooked cross in red enamel, suspension bar.
From £1,000

HP-28092
'Peachey Family'
Heraldic Horse
Harness Pendant
34mm
White enamelled field with
red bar and two chevrons.
£120 - £180

HP-30030
'William de Valoynes' Heraldic
Horse Harness Pendant
48mm
Three red and white wavy lines.
£100 - £150

HP-21089
Heraldic Horse
Harness Pendant
37mm
Reserved trefoil
motif on red and blue
enamelled field.
£40 - £60

HP-40665
Silvered Horse
Harness Pendant
76mm
Reserved eight-pointed
star, rosettes between
the points.
£80 - £120

HP-26451
Heraldic Horse
Harness Pendant
25mm
Red and blue
enamelled segments.
£20 - £30

HP-37917
Heraldic Horse Harness
Pendant with Hanger
40mm
Red enamel with reserved
square.
£80 - £120

HP-37918
Heraldic
Horse Harness
Pendant
41mm
Blue enamelled
panel, reserved
rosette motif.
£50 - £80

HP-37919
Heraldic Openwork Horse
Harness Pendant
90mm
Rosette and regardant beast
motifs; Iberian workmanship.
From £800

HP-40604
Three-Part
Heraldic
Horse Harness
Pendant
63mm
Red and blue
enamel with three
leaves conjoined.
£100 - £150

HP-T0110
Heraldic
Pendant
23mm
Religious text
'AVE MARIA
GRACIE' (Hail
Mary [full of]
Grace) and heater
shield.
From £300

HP-40609
Escutcheon Heraldic Horse Harness Pendant
32mm
Escutcheon with incised cross, text in Lombardic script 'AVE MARIA GRAT[IA PLENA] 'Hail Mary full of Grace'.

£100 - £150

HP-T0109
Heraldic Harness Pendant
64mm
Westminster Abbey type.

From £500

HP-15753
Heraldic Horse Harness Pendant
36mm
Text in Lombardic capitals '+AVEMARIAGRACIA' for Ave Maria Gratia Plena 'Hail Mary full of Grace'.

£120 - £180

HP-40326
Heraldic Horse
Harness Pendant
45mm
Semé-de-lis design
(repeating pattern of
fleurs-de-lis).
£50 - £80

HP-25941
Heraldic Horse
Harness Pendant
Group
29-43mm
One with two mullets
in chief gilded on
a recessed field for
champ-levé enamel; one
with a red fess on a blue
and white paly field.
£100 - £150

HP-14820
Heraldic Horse Harness Pendant
54mm
Fleurs-de-lys on a green enamelled field and a hackle on a red field.
£50 - £80

HP-7355
Heraldic Horse Harness Pendant
66mm
Shield with horizontal bars, foliage surrounding.
£150 - £200

HP-4852
Heraldic Horse Harness Pendant
44mm
White enamelled lion rampant.
£100 - £150

HP-38504
St Thomas Becket
Horse Harness
Pendant
39mm
Openwork facing
peacock.
£50 - £80

HP-15166
'Isabella' Horse
Harness Pendant
65mm
Gilt crown over a 'Y'
between leaves.
£100 - £150

HP-15167
Gothic Spandrel
Horse Harness
Pendant
77mm
Spandrel with
superimposed 'M'.
£50 - £80

HP-40329
Enamelled Horse
Harness Pendant
79mm
Reserved profile figure
seated on a throne within
an arch.
£200 - £300

HP-40328
Enamelled
Horse
Harness
Pendant
37mm
Reserved figure
of a horse and
rider.
£100 - £150

HP-15050
Horse Harness Pendant
58mm
Blue enamel field with red
and blue enamelled pellets.
£80 - £120

HP-40643
Horse Harness
Pendant
40mm
Palmette with alternating
hatched and scrolled
leaves.
£20 - £30

HP-21105
Horse Harness
Pendant
62mm
Lions rampant on the disc;
with hanger.
£200 - £300

HP-T0107
Horse Harness Pendant
54mm
Religious motif of 'Pelican in her Piety'.
£150 - £200

HP-6253
Horse Harness
Mount and
Pendant
49mm
Beaded field with
central escutcheon.
£80 - £120

HP-44866
'Andrews Family' Horse
Harness Pendant
41mm
Blue enamelled field with gold
saltire and four crosses in the
quarters.
£100 - £150

HP-18363
Horse Harness
Pendant
52mm
Rosette with blue
and red enamel to
the petals.
£80 - £120

HP-23327
Horse Harness
Pendant
with Arabic
Monogram
65mm
Monogram of
'Allah' and 'S K'
in Arabic script;
Spanish type.
£200 - £300

HP-30061
Horse Harness
Pendant
45mm
Gilt-bronze
cruciform
pendant.
£10 - £20

HP-48044
Openwork Horse
Harness Strap
Junction
79mm
Mesh of scrolled tendrils
and hatched panels.
£120 - £180

HM-9824
'John of Brittany, 3rd
Earl of Richmond'
Heraldic Mount
68mm
Checky escutcheon with
border of passant lions and
an ermine canton.
£300 - £400

HM-6708
'Humphrey de Bohun' Armorial Horse Bridle Mount
77mm
Diagonal bar and six lions rampant.
£200 - £300

HM-11193
Limoges 'Earl of Norfolk' Heraldic Box Mount
66mm
Gilt and green field with lion rampant.
£120 - £180

HM-23098
'Earl of Norfolk' Reliquary Box Mount
64mm
Lion rampant on red enamel field.
£100 - £150

HM-12523
'Royal Arms of
England' Heraldic
Mount
29mm
Three lions passant on a
red enamelled field.
£30 - £50

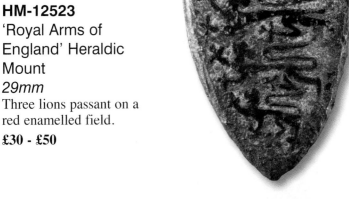

HM-41975
Heraldic Lion Mask
Mount
31mm
Gilt-bronze lion mask
pierced in five places.
£100 - £150

HM-20281
'Scottish' Heraldic
Mount
47mm
Reserved lion rampant on
red enamelled field.
£50 - £80

HM-33357
Heraldic Belt
Mount
31mm
Lion passant
gardant modelled
in the half-round.
£80 - £120

HM-26746
Heraldic
Horse Harness
Mount
65mm
Enamelled bronze
bifacial mount
with lion and
eagle.
£120 - £180

HM-T0129
Heraldic
Mount
29mm
Lion rampant
type.
£50 - £80

HM-40995
'Gardiner Family'
Griffin Heraldic
Mount
38mm
Griffin passant
regardant.
£30 - £50

HM-38381
Openwork Heraldic
Belt Mount
24mm
Reserved hound motif.
£50 - £80

HM-23330
Heraldic Dog Mount
77mm
Leaping dog with hatched panels; Spanish type.
£50 - £80

HM-1815
'Sir Geoffrey Luttrell'
Enamelled Heraldic
Mount
53mm
Enamelled bar between
six birds.
From £1,000

HP-T0106
Heraldic Harness
Mount
40mm
Stork motif.
£150 - £200

HM-43426
Eagle in Wreath
Heraldic Mount
60mm
Rectangular cells on the
wreath below the chest.
£50 - £80

HP-40619
'James Stanley' Heraldic Horse Harness Mount
64mm
Cock's claw with coronet above.
£100 - £150

HM-18103
Stag-Head Heraldic Mount
90mm
Heraldic 'collared stag' device modelled in the round.
£200 - £300

HM-40883
Silver-Gilt Heraldic 'Sir William Stanley' Stag-Head Mount
32mm
Facing stag's head with four-tine antlers.
£50 - £80

HM-26744
'Latimer Family'
Heraldic Mount
32mm
Red enamelled field with
reserved cross patoncé.
£120 - £180

HM-40621
'Raoul of Clermont'
Heraldic Horse
Harness Mount
60mm
Red enamelled field with
reserved trefoils and two
vertical barbels.
£200 - £300

HP-31943
'De Cockfeld Family'
Heraldic Horse Harness
Mount
36mm
Red enamel with silver
fleurs de lis.
£100 - £150

HM-17952
'Bishopsdale Family'
Heraldic Harness
Mount
18mm
Eight diagonal bars.
£40 - £60

HM-21549
Horse Harness Mount
30mm
Red enamelled with reserved
gilt enthroned figure of a king,
crowned with a sceptre in the
left hand.
£50 - £80

HM-41502
Heraldic Openwork
Mount
140mm
Openwork lead tracery
with central rosette.
£50 - £80

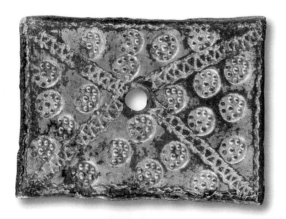

HM-23084
Heraldic Mount
with Saltire
42mm
Incised saltire with
four sets of punched
rosettes.
£20 - £30

HM-38873
Horse Harness
Mount
33mm
Radiating petals
within a beaded
border.
£30 - £40

HM-4984
Quatrefoil Mount
58mm
Reserved 'W'
formed from four
intersecting drinking
horns, red enamel
infill.
£50 - £80

HM-33400
Horse Harness Strap
Mount
44mm
Four radiating trefoils
pierced at the centre.
£50 - £120

HM-T0131
Heraldic Roundel
Mount
40mm
Lion mask motif;
Tudor type.
£300 - £500

HM-T0119
Heraldic
Belt Plate
54mm
Sea lion
regardant
motif.
£300 - £400

HM-T0120
Heraldic Badge
33mm
Rampant Lion royalist
motif.
£80 - £120

HS-21649
'Bruce of Skelton'
Heraldic Horse
Harness Stud
30mm
Enamelled field with
reserved rampant lion.
£80 - £120

HS-26428
Heraldic Horse
Harness Stud
27mm
Three lions to the left
and a field of fleurs-de-
lys to the right.
£40 - £60

HS-26749
Heraldic Horse
Harness Finial
29mm
Standing dragon with
spread wings and curled
tail.
£100 - £150

HS-30050
Scottish 'Philip de la
Lea' Heraldic Horse
Harness Stud
33mm
Enamelled arms of six
birds with a transverse bar
between, the outer edges
stepped.
£50 - £80

HS-42190
Heraldic Horse
Harness Stud
28mm
Blue enamelled field with
reserved eagle rising.
£100 - £150

HS-40612
Heraldic Horse
Harness Stud
34mm
Reserved splayed
eagle.
£50 - £80

HS-21561
Heraldic Horse
Harness Stud
36mm
Enamelled blue field with
heater shield within, red
border with saltires and
standing bird motif.
£80 - £120

HS-33402
Horse Harness Stud
22mm
Blue enamel with
reserved house with
D-shaped doorway,
opposed birds to the
roof.
£100 - £150

HS-40611
Heraldic Horse
Harness Stud
33mm
Reserved animal to each
lobe, bird in flight to the
centre.
£20 - £30

HS-12486
Welsh 'Sir John
ap Adam' Heraldic
Enamelled Horse
Harness Stud
21mm
Enamelled red cross on a
silver field with five gold
stars.
£80 - £120

HS-26431
'John de Warenne'
Heraldic Horse
Harness Stud
17mm
Blue enamelled squares.
£50 - £80

HS-17256
'Bardulf Family'
Heraldic Horse
Harness Stud
31mm
Three white cinquefoils
on a blue enamel field.
£100 - £150

HS-16477
'Sir Robert de
Tibetot' Heraldic
Stud
29mm
Incised saltire engrailed.
£80 - £120

MO-52855
Heraldic Mount
42mm
Red enamel border,
three blue enamel bars.
£80 - £120

MO-51490
Silver Double-Headed Eagle Mount
32mm
Double-headed eagle with heater shield to the chest, crown between the heads.
£80 - £120

MO-48791
Lion Mount
49mm
Enamelled field with reserved lion passant gardant, Norman type.
£200 - £300

MO-52240
Heraldic Lion Horse Harness Mount
27mm
Lion passant regardant, Continental type.
£40 - £60

MO-53082
Gilt Harness Mount
32mm
Reserved bird-head
£80 - £120

MO-48073
Heraldic Lion Head
Mount
25mm
Facing lion mask.
£30 - £40

MO-48525
Jewellery Box Mount
39mm
Silver inlaid floral tracery.
£50 - £80

MO-48207
Reliquary Box Mount
66mm
Blue enamelled panel with three
flowers.
£50 - £80

MO-50753
Heraldic Panther Mount
48mm
Panther with forelegs extended.
£50 - £80

MO-50509
Gilt Mount
35mm
Openwork
dragon,
hinged loop.
£40 - £60

MO-52430
Gilt Mount
26mm
Youthful face
in a beaded
border.
£30 - £40

MO-52428
Domed
Mount
65mm
Openwork
foliage and
rearing beast.
£80 - £120

MO-53088
Belt Mount
42mm
Regardant lion.
£30 - £40

MO-53245
Gilt Mount
35mm
Two standing birds
in foliage.
£80 - £120

MO-52230
Horse Harness
Mount
47mm
Openwork
regardant beast.
£80 - £120

MO-39427
Gilt Mount
13mm
Silver-gilt bird with
wings partly spread.
£50 - £80

MO-50032
Decorated
Plaque
63mm
Incised female face
in profile.
£80 - £120

MO-43405
Gilt Mount
15mm
Silver-gilt,
quatrefoil motif.
£50 - £80

MO-43623
Book Mount
57mm
Winged lion of St
Mark with mouth
open.
£100 - £150

MO-42646
Gilt Mount
15mm
Gargoyle mask.
£40 - £60

MO-45171
Fish Plaque
63mm
Two entwined fish with trefoil tails.
£40 - £60

MO-43281
Appliqué Pair
41-44mm
Leaping lion with forelegs extended.
£100 - £150

MO-43282
Lion's Head Appliqué
38mm
Lion mask with radiating mane, pierced at the ears and mouth.

£30 - £50

MO-43283
Birds Mount
85mm
Byzantine-influenced opposed birds.

£80 - £120

MO-45899
Appliqué Pair
48-54mm
Carved bone crowns.
£80 - £120

MO-43877
Panel Pair
79-82mm
Pair of bone panels, each
with profile face and
rosettes.
£80 - £120

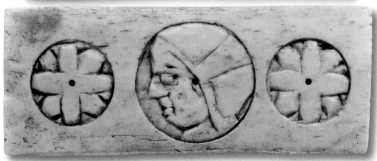

MO-43878
Panel Pair
125mm
Pair of bone panels, each with
heater shield and figures below.
£150 - £200

We are accepting single entries and collections of coins and antiquities

Greek Gold Pin with Sphinx

Central London
Auction Venue

TimeLine Auctions Limited
The Court House
363 Main Road
Harwich, Essex
CO12 4DN

www.timelineauctions.com

+44 [0]1277 815121
enquiries@timelineauctions.com

RELIGIOUS AND FIGURAL ITEMS

Representations of the human figure became a common feature of medieval art.

The most important of these culturally were the images of Christ and the various saints used in religious contexts. Christ appears regularly as the Corpus Christi nailed to the cross of Calvary wearing just a loincloth and a crown of thorns. Some versions include a halo, but this was often made separately for practical reasons where it was silvered or gilded.

Figures of saints appear on a variety of ecclesiastical objects including shrines and screens, where they are often shown with their customary symbols.

Military figures appear regularly, often in the form of chessmen, with details of their armour and heraldry carefully depicted. Heraldic items of all kinds are widely collected, especially if the arms can be tied to a particular family. Changing fashions in weaponry and armour allow such images to be fairly closely dated.

The range of pilgrim items is broad, with ampullae, flasks, religious pendants and badges the most easily identifiable. The places of pilgrimage can often be identified from the imagery and from the known distribution of these artefacts.

Purse bars from which the fabric or leather bag was suspended often show religious imagery or bear a text appealing to a saint for assistance and protection.

Figural items of various kinds are a popular subject for collectors who may concentrate on specific aspects such as the pilgrimage routes, or the representations of a particular saint.

FS-T0106
Gaming Piece
49mm
Armoured horseman
with kite shield and
surcoat; Norman or
Angevin type.
From £5,000

FS-3943
Crucifix Figure
110mm
Corpus Christi;
Norman type.
£1,000 - £1,500

FS-42180
Limoges Corpus
Christi Figurine
76mm
Gilt-bronze with inset black
glass eyes, enamelled panels on
the loincloth.
From £800

FS-3999
Corpus Christi
Figurine
120mm
Bone, loincloth
supported by a cord.
£400 - £600

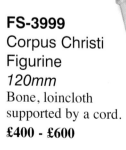

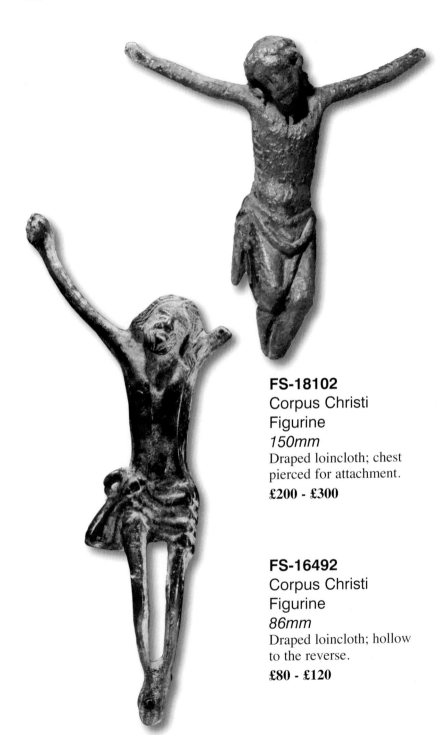

FS-18102
Corpus Christi
Figurine
150mm
Draped loincloth; chest
pierced for attachment.
£200 - £300

FS-16492
Corpus Christi
Figurine
86mm
Draped loincloth; hollow
to the reverse.
£80 - £120

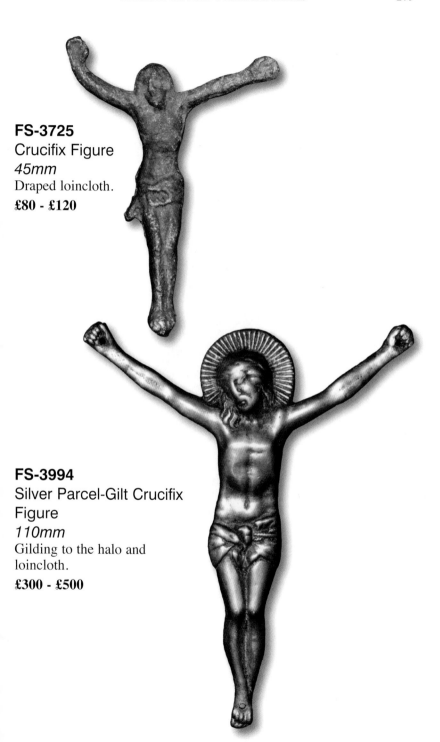

FS-3725
Crucifix Figure
45mm
Draped loincloth.
£80 - £120

FS-3994
Silver Parcel-Gilt Crucifix
Figure
110mm
Gilding to the halo and
loincloth.
£300 - £500

FS-48060
Seated Monk
Figurine
52mm
With cap, cowl and
short-sleeved tunic.
£200 - £300

FS-44856
Silver-Gilt St Peter
Figurine
34mm
St Peter with halo,
book and key; gilding
almost complete.
£150 - £200

FS-39928
Silver Figurine
31mm
Wimpled lady in long
robe.
£150 - £200

FS-T0104
Heraldic Figurine
42mm
Lion couchant motif.
£300-£500

FS-41493
Lion Figurine
38mm
Bronze, reclining with head
turned.
£100 - £150

FS-18388
Silver-Gilt Eagle
Figurine
17mm
Finial, eagle with wings
spread.
£100 - £150

FS-18374
Purse Hanger
60mm
Bronze monk figure, hollow
to the rear with loop below.
£50 - £80

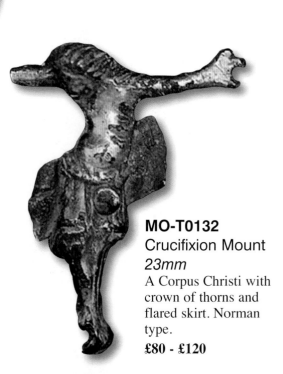

MO-T0132
Crucifixion Mount
23mm
A Corpus Christi with
crown of thorns and
flared skirt. Norman
type.
£80 - £120

MO-7853
Silver-Gilt
Ornamental Mount
31mm
Foliage design, gilded
with niello detail.
£400 - £600

MO-3447
Silver-Gilt Apostle Mounts
55-58mm
Five apostles St Andrew (St Andrew's cross), St Peter (keys), St John
(quill), St Thomas (pilgrim's staff) and St Paul (sword).
£2,500 - £3,500

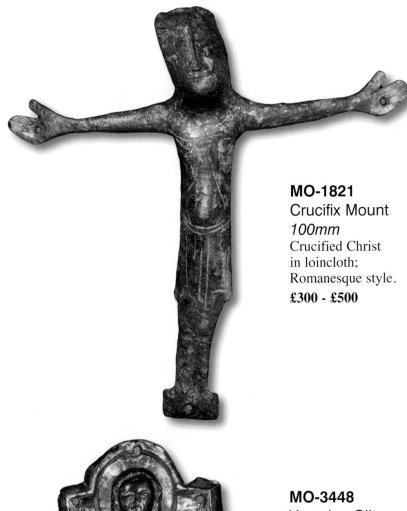

MO-1821
Crucifix Mount
100mm
Crucified Christ
in loincloth;
Romanesque style.
£300 - £500

MO-3448
Venetian Gilt
Cross Mount
81mm
Female with long
hair, loose robe and
mantle, arms raised
to her chest.
From £500

MO-1822
Processional Cross Mount
54mm
Ecclesiastical architectural style with four gables on a background of arched windows.
£150 - £200

MO-13916
Limoges Cross Mount
80mm
Garment with radiating panels in green enamel.
£300 - £500

MO-22575
Corpus Christi
Mount
83mm
Christ with
outstretched arms,
nimbus to the rear.
£80 - £120

MO-T0130
Figural Mount
30mm
Mary Magdalene
motif.
£150 - £200

MO-2327
Figural Mount
48mm
Female saint in draped garments, right hand clutching the left breast.
£80 - £120

MO-785
Figural
Mount
51mm
Virgin Mary in
loose robes.
£50 - £80

MO-24696
Figural Mount
39mm
Robed figure with a staff in the right hand and a lamb in the crook of the left arm, representing St Agnes with lily and lamb.
£40 - £60

MO-16485
Limoges Figural Saint Mount
58mm
Enamelled cellwork to the body.
£30 - £50

MO-2404
Gilt Figural Mount
125mm
Tunic with raised acanthus-leaf designs, legs
with horse-hoof finials; heavy gilding.
£400 - £600

MO-6723
Limoges Enamelled
Figural Plaque
64mm
Panels of white enamel, fine
facial features and black glass
bead eyes.
£300 - £500

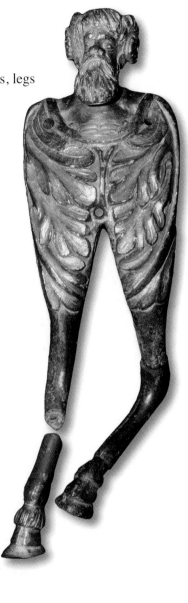

MO-T0133
Figural Limoges Mount
55mm
Cellwork to the body with blue enamel.
£150 - £200

MO-20280
Limoges Figural Mount
71mm
Cellwork to the body to accept enamel.
£50 - £80

MO-24408
Silver-Gilt Figural
Mount
17mm
Two figures in an arcade
within a frame; French
type.
£80 - £120

MO-24284
Royal Figural
Mount
56mm
Crowned and cloaked
figure seated with right
hand on one knee.
£100 - £150

MO-3623
Figural Mount
88mm
Bearded male in loose robe, book in left hand, right hand raised in blessing.
£100 - £150

MO-22578
Shrine Head Mount
82mm
Female head with crespines flanking the face.
£100 - £150

MO-22598
Shrine Head Mount
47mm
Female head with crespines flanking the face.
£100 - £150

MO-20985
Monk's Bust Mount
19mm
Monk's head modelled in the round.
£40 - £60

MO-18130
Silver Iconographic Mount
12mm
Two nimbate robed figures embracing.
£100 - £150

MO-43758
Iconographic Mount
49mm
St Barbara with palm branch symbol in her right hand, Christ child in her left hand.
£80 - £120

MO-43750
Ecclesiastical
Mount
39mm
Virgin Mary seated
with infant Jesus on her
left knee.
£80 - £120

MO-19593
Mount with Female
Figure
44mm
Figure with left hand
raised, right hand
clutching the robe.
£80 - £120

MO-T0134
Belt Mount
32mm
Swordsman motif.
£150 - £200

MO-9758
Horseman Scabbard
Mount
36mm
Helmetted horseman
with teardrop shield on
a caparisoned horse,
axe over his shoulder.
Norman type.
£40 - £60

MO-16364
Stone Face Mount
73mm
Luxuriant beard and
hair, diadem above the
brow.
£50 - £80

MO-3900
Silver Hand of
Benediction
Tapestry Mount
110mm
Pierced at the wrist
and finger-tip for
attachment.
£100 - £150

MO-1826
Mask Mount
34mm
Human face above a
triangular plate with
a lancet motif.
£100 - £150

MO-13765
Head Mount
47mm
Bronze vessel mount.
£80 - £120

MO-9930
Gilt Bird Mount
38mm
Bird with human head,
hatched body; Norman type.
£150 - £200

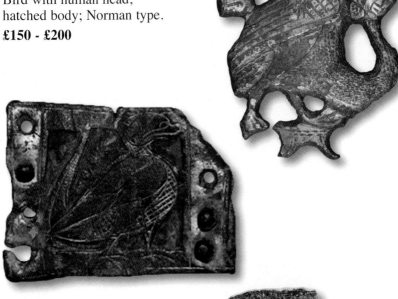

MO-T0135
Limoges Mount
38mm
Bird motif.
£200 - £300

MO-4295
Limoges Mount
59mm
Enamelled eagle with raised
wings; Anglo-Norman type.
£60 - £90

MO-37499
Openwork Horse
Harness Mount
59mm
Openwork duck
among foliage, inlaid
copper detailing to
wings and breast;
Norman type.
£200 - £300

MO-19290
Romanesque
Openwork Mount
26mm
Advancing bird in a
circular frame; gilded;
Norman type.
£100 - £150

MO-1824
Mount
43mm
Cherub motif; Tudor
type.
£30 - £50

MO-14453
Enamelled
Limoges Mount
56mm
Nimbate angel
(symbol of St
Matthew) on red and
blue enamelled field;
traces of gilding.
£150 - £200

MO-T0136
Limoges Plaque
57mm
Lion of St Mark
motif.
£400 - £600

MO-8959
Religious Mount
77mm
Lion of St Mark
motif.
£300 - £500

MO-T0137
Religious
Mount
57mm
Lion of St Mark
motif.
£50 - £80

MO-34830
Enamelled
Limoges
Mount
58mm
Red and blue
enamel lion of St
Mark; Norman
type.
£80 - £120

MO-37906
Silver Lion
Head Mount
15mm
Pellet eyes, slot
mouth, fur texture.
£100 - £150

MO-T0138
Gilded Mount
21mm
Lion's face design.
£100 - £150

MO-34487
Leaping Beast Mount
23mm
Reserved pouncing lion
among foliage; Norman
type.
£30 - £50

MO-18366
Griffin Mount
19mm
High relief figure of a
griffin; gilded; Norman
type.
£120 - £180

MO-12526
Mount
19mm
Gilt-bronze, beast
motif.
£40 - £60

MO-18116
Strap Mount
with Beast
Head Terminal
41mm
Body and limbs of
a beast, pierced;
Norman type.
£80 - £120

MO-5900
Enamelled
Quatrefoil
Mount
55mm
Passant beast with
coiled tail.
£80 - £120

MO-28029
Triple Beast-
Headed Mount
20mm
Romanesque style
beast head with
curved extensions above,
terminating in smaller heads;
Norman type.
£150 - £200

MO-28024
Silver Beast-
Headed Mount
26mm
Beast head
finial and
curved bars
with beast-head
finials; Norman type
£150 - £200

MO-3727
Otter Mount
63mm
Scallopped outline and punched dot
detailing; gilded.
£50 - £80

MO-3676
Enamelled
Cross Bottony
Belt Mount
26mm
Cross bottony
reserved on a
blue enamel
background.
£50 - £80

MO-20983
Silver
Epigraphic
Mount
Fragment
23mm
Blackletter text
'MELCHOR' and
rosette.
£20 - £30

MO-3728
Harness Mount
62mm
Quadrate cross
with reclining dog
panel.
£40 - £60

MO-T0139
Limoges Mount
40mm
Figure with crossed arms.
£150 - £200

MO-26752
Enamelled Strap
Junction Mount
26mm
Blue enamel fill to the cell.
£50 - £80

MO-4930
Limoges Mount
52mm
Enamelled floral scrollwork.
£40 - £60

MO-4879
Cruciform Mount
42mm
Cross potent with
ribbed arms.
£40 - £60

MO-8653
Gilded Harness
Mount
63mm
Openwork cruciform
design, gilding
remaining.
£20 - £40

MO-28383
Leather Mount
15mm
Repoussé fret on a
textured field.
£20 - £30

MO-18336
Knight Book Mount
51mm
Armoured and cloaked, with hands raised in prayer.
£200 - £300

MO-37905
Silver-Gilt Book Mount
67mm
St Nicholas facing wearing a mitre.
£300 - £500

MO-2042
Bible Box Mount
68mm
Crucifixion scene with a figure either side under a gothic arch.
£150 - £200

MO-31209
Book Mount
51mm
Lady with purse motif.
£100 - £150

MO-31211
Book Mount
32mm
£30 - £40

MO-5637
Gold Book Mount
14mm
Fleur-de-lis outlined in
beaded wire; Norman
type.
£150 - £200

MO-20093
Silver Book Mount
51mm
Griffin with right
foreleg extended, wing
spread.
£120 - £180

MO-7816
Book Mount
18mm
Advancing beast with extended tongue;
gilded.
£80 - £120

MO-25542
Silver-
Gilt Book
Clasp
25mm
Madonna
and Child
motif.
£50 - £80

MO-37990
Enamelled
Limoges
Casket Mount
56mm
Parcel-gilt male
head, body with
panels of red
and blue enamel.
£50 - £80

MO-6227
Limoges Enamelled Saint Casket
Mount
88mm
Standing figure with long robe and wimple in
green enamel within an arch.
£80 - £120

MO-24623
Reliquary
Casket Mount
38mm
Blue, white,
black, yellow
and red enamel;
Limoges
or Moselle
workmanship.
£50 - £80

MO-11199
Limoges Reliquary Box Mount
100mm
Reserved design of a castle, a standing robed female
and dove in flight.
£20 - £30

MO-23572
Morning Star
Scabbard
Mount
38mm
Gilt-bronze,
pyramid with
triangular
extensions.
£20 - £30

MO-18114
Gold Panel
15mm
Fleur-de-lis motif; Norman
type.
From £400

DF-28018
Beast's Head Finial
33mm
Hunting dog's head
moulded in the round;
gilded.
£200 - £300

NS-3748
Gold Stud
35mm
Opposed pair of Lombardic
'M' characters.
£200 - £300

DF-39927
Fitting with Beast Heads
47mm
Beast-head finials and recurved arm; Norman type.

£50 - £80

DF-18126
Decorative Fitting
26mm
Quatrefoil mount with central void.

£40 - £60

DF-26472
Wolf-Heads Finial
21mm
Two upturned wolf-heads with fur texture; Norman type.

£50 - £70

NS-16765
Lion Harness Stud
32mm
Reserved mask on
enamelled field.
£20 - £30

NS-17046
Harness Link
39mm
Rectangular with central
void and slots to the four
sides.
£20 - £30

ST-45501
Silver-Gilt Strap End
26mm
Hatched chevron motifs.
£80 - £120

ST-3640
Strap End
63mm
Incised 'IE' in
blackletter script,
openwork figure of
Madonna and Child.
£80 - £120

ST-15168
Strap Slider with Acorn
Pendants
62mm
Lancet arches and trefoils,
two pendant acorns.
£20 - £30

PI-6677
Crusader Glass Cup
110mm
Translucent blue glass with applied designs in red and yellow. Ayyubid workmanship.

From £1,000

PI-10611
Portable Altar with
34mm
Miniature pewter altar, Madonna and Child between two candlesticks.

£400 - £600

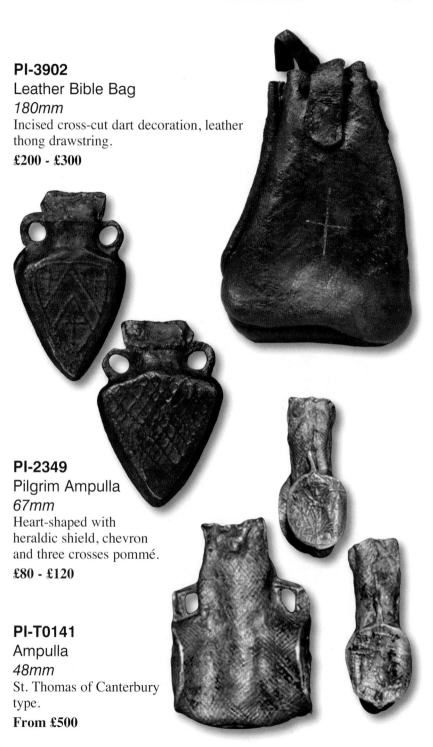

PI-3902
Leather Bible Bag
180mm
Incised cross-cut dart decoration, leather
thong drawstring.
£200 - £300

PI-2349
Pilgrim Ampulla
67mm
Heart-shaped with
heraldic shield, chevron
and three crosses pommé.
£80 - £120

PI-T0141
Ampulla
48mm
St. Thomas of Canterbury
type.
From £500

PI-T0142
Pilgrim's
Ampulla
34mm
Heraldic shields
design.
£150 - £200

PI-16489
Pilgrim's
Ampulla
48mm
Lead-alloy,
two lateral
attachment
lugs, bands
of hatched
ornament to
each face.
£50 - £80

PI-37910
Pilgrim's
Ampulla
60mm
Scallop to one
face, merchant's
mark of shield
with cross
motif.
£50 - £80

PI-T0143
Pilgrim's
Ampulla
55mm
Cross and
chevron motifs.
£100 - £150

PI-18328
Pilgrim's Ampulla
48mm
Lead, with two loop handles
to the neck.
£50 - £80

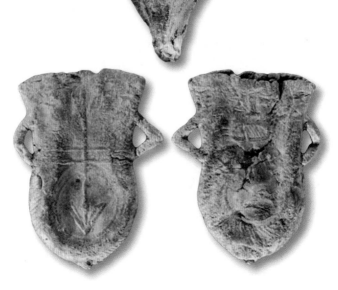

PI-T0144
Pilgrim's
Ampulla
28mm
Long
Arrow of
Walsingham
motif.
£50-£80

PI-47596
Pilgrim's Ampulla
52mm
Scallop to one face
and chevrons to the
other.
£30 - £50

PI-16050
Fish-Shaped
Pilgrim's Ampulla
180mm
Punched-point
geometric detail.
£30 - £40

PI-18329
Pilgrim's Flask
95mm
Concentric rings to
each face.
£30 - £40

PI-3217
Clay
Figural
Pilgrim's
Flask
86mm
Sun-in-
splendour
motif.
£50 - £80

PI-3218
Ceramic Pilgrim
Flask
80mm
Three boss feet,
two suspension
loops.
£30 - £40

PI-28032
Silver-Gilt St Edward the
Confessor Pilgrim's Badge
39mm
Openwork brooch, capital 'E' with fleur-
de-lys tracery ornamentation, parcel-gilt.
£1,200 - £1,800

PI-16370
'St Thomas Becket' Pilgrim Badge
68mm
Bust of Thomas Becket with chasuble and mitre.
From £300

PI-2360
Figural Pilgrim Belt Set
31mm
Ten pewter links and two-part hook-and-eye fastening, depicting crowned Thomas Becket busts, mitred bishop's heads, horse heads and turretted towers, some with gilding.
From £300

PI-43544
'Henry V' Silver-Gilt Coin
Pilgrim's Badge
25mm
Facing bust in tressure with
mullet on right shoulder and
'+HENRIC DI GRA REXANGL
Z FRANC' legend; long cross and
pellets dividing '+POSVIDEVM
A DIVTOR E MEVM AND
CIVITASLON DON' legends for
London mint.

£400 - £600

PI-19621
Pilgrim Badge
56mm
Bust of Thomas Becket with
chasuble and mitre.

£200 - £300

PI-44457
Pilgrim's Badge
26mm
'Our Lady Mary of Willesden' crowned and with a sceptre, standing in a crescent boat with beaded lower edge.
£180 - £240

PI-44456
'St. Thomas Becket' Pilgrim's Badge
24mm
Integral pin to the reverse.
£150 - £200

PI-44455
Pilgrim's Badge
61mm
Standing robed archbishop Thomas Becket; openwork fillets joined by rosettes.
£300 - £500

PI-30415
Pewter Jousting Badge
31mm
A mounted horseman with canted shield and tilting helm.

£300 - £500

PI-38096
Pilgrim's Badge
25mm
Nimbate St Barbara and holding a palm frond, tower with three windows.

£100 - £150

PI-2622
Pilgrim's Badge
47mm
Mounted nimbate knight striking with a lance into the mouth of a dragon.

£100 - £150

PI-T0145
Pilgrim's Badge
17mm
Saint George and the dragon motif.
£200 - £300

PI-37486
Pilgrim Badge
100mm
Concentric bands of scrolled foliage, scene of Calvary with Corpus Christi and two kneeling figures.
£80 - £120

PI-32974
Pilgrim's Badge
21mm
Openwork pewter badge, Christ's head in three-quarter view within a ring.
£150 - £200

PI-38158
Pilgrim's Badge
25mm
Fish with forked tail and hatched body, two spread wings.
£80 - £120

PI-19630
Pilgrim's Badge
19mm
Running cockerel with spurs to the rear of the feet.
£150 - £200

PI-31385
Pilgrim Badge
35mm
King David enthroned,
holding the head of Goliath
in one hand and Goliath's
sword in the other.

£200 - £300

PI-7240
Pilgrim's Badge
48mm
Tethered swan with collar
and loop, standing on a
scroll with script and loop
below.

£500 - £800

PI-3746
Pilgrim's Badge
30mm
Mary and child with text
above 'AVE.MARIA.
MARIA.PU'.

£50 - £80

PI-3745
Pilgrim's Badges
28-31mm
One a Madonna and Child
figure with incised lettering
'vgn.mar' to the reverse; the
other a nimbate Mary and
child with sceptre.

£100 - £150

PI-8724
Silver-Gilt
Scrolled
Pilgrim's
Badge
33mm
Central cross
with stitching
holes on each
arm.

£50 - £80

PI-7300
'Saints Peter and Paul'
Pilgrim's Badge
43mm
Two figures, one with mitre
and robes, lozenge-headed
staff and cross above; text
in rustic capitals 'SPE SPA'
above the figures.

£100 - £150

PI-18068
Pilgrim's Badge
25mm
Robed saint holding a
long cross in left hand,
right hand raised in
blessing.
£20 - £30

PI-30412
Pewter Hunting Horn
Badge
21mm
Hunting horn of St Hubert
motif.
£50 - £80

PI-30414
Pewter Pilgrim's
badge
15mm
A plough in profile with
openwork crown above,
for 'Plough Monday'.
£50 - £80

PI-T0146
Pilgrim's
Purse Badge
59mm
Expanding-arm
cross type.
£100 - £150

PI-33764
Horseman Badge
33mm
Pewter horseman with
tilting helm, lance and
shield.
£80 - £120

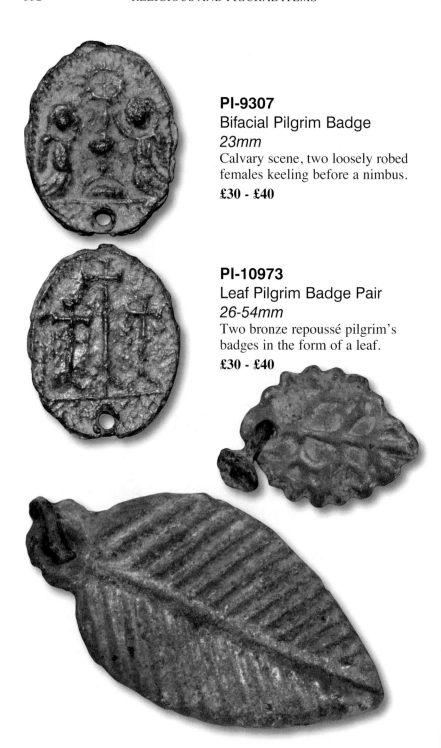

PI-9307
Bifacial Pilgrim Badge
23mm
Calvary scene, two loosely robed females keeling before a nimbus.
£30 - £40

PI-10973
Leaf Pilgrim Badge Pair
26-54mm
Two bronze repoussé pilgrim's badges in the form of a leaf.
£30 - £40

PI-12453
Livery Badge
34mm
Plantagenet 'Sun, Moon
and Star' design.
£20 - £30

PI-T0147
Bracteate
15mm
Knights of
the Holy
Sepulchre
type.
£20 - £30

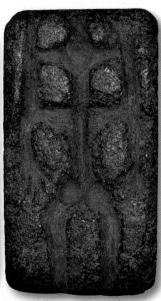

PI-1368
Pilgrim
Badge
Mould
52mm
Stone two-sided mould for casting badges, one side showing an
oval with a superimposed sword, the other an openwork rectangular
design.
£50 - £80

CP-50738
Gilt Pendant
36mm
Griffin with raised
tail and fleur-de-lys
wing.
£150 - £200

CP-51092
Gilt Pendant
Group
24-42mm
Filigree, pendants
with granules.
£100 - £140

CP-50110
Pendant
26mm
Serpent with looped
tail.
£80 - £120

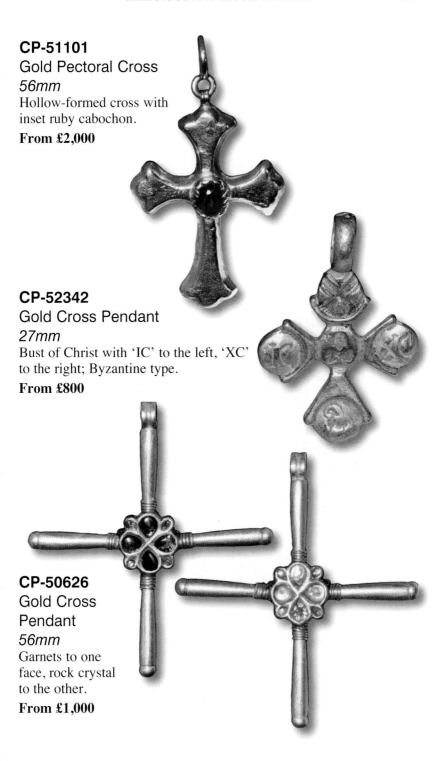

CP-51101
Gold Pectoral Cross
56mm
Hollow-formed cross with inset ruby cabochon.
From £2,000

CP-52342
Gold Cross Pendant
27mm
Bust of Christ with 'IC' to the left, 'XC' to the right; Byzantine type.
From £800

CP-50626
Gold Cross
Pendant
56mm
Garnets to one face, rock crystal to the other.
From £1,000

CP-51835
Gold Cross
Pendant
32mm
Filigree scrolls, inset
garnet cabochon;
Byzantine type
From £800

CP-43759
Knight and
Dragon Pendant
23mm
Openwork plaque,
horseman trampling
a dragon.
£10 - £20

CP-43353
Silver Pendant
58mm
Repoussé lion on a
hatched field.
£120 - £180

CP-43893
Gold
Touchpiece
Pendant
28mm
Based on an
Écu d'Or à la
Chaise coin,
pierced for use
as a touchpiece.
£100 - £140

PI-3923
Pilgrim's Pendant
43mm
Angel on one face, cross on the
other.
£80 - £120

CP-44954
Hammer
Pendant
44mm
Claw hammer
with loop above
the head.
£20 - £30

PI-12525
Silver Pendant
25mm
Discoid plaque with
severed head of
John the Baptist on a
platter.
£100 - £150

PI-21640
Pilgrim's Pendant
32mm
Pewter St Margaret
plaque, 'IHS' to the
reverse for IHSOS
'Jesus'.
£50 - £80

PI-42030
Pilgrim's Whistle
39mm
Pewter with scrolled plaque
above.
£120 - £180

PI-43401
Pilgrim's Whistle
36mm
Bulb with rib, vent and
integral suspension ring.
£100 - £150

PI-T0148
Pilgrim's Whistle
39mm
Brass, 'St Catherine's
Wheel' motif.
£50 - £80

PB-7830
Purse Frame
205mm
Inscribed.
£500 - £800

PB-7387
Purse Bar
160mm
Gilt panel with
engraved 'Tears of
Christ' design.
£200 - £300

PB-7386
Inscribed Purse Bar
150mm
Inlaid silver saltires and fretwork, 'IHS' (Jesus) inscription.
£80 - £120

PB-4019
Inscribed Purse Bar
110mm
Inscribed 'NTOME IAMEN' and
'MATER DEI ME' to the outer
faces and IHS and M to the boss;
some niello inlay.
£80 - £120

PB-T0113
Purse Bar
146mm
With inscription.
£80 - £120

PB-4352
Hinged Purse Bar
93mm
Trefoil pendant to each face, two makers' marks to the frame.
£80 - £120

PB-16318
Purse Bar
44mm
Rectangular loop, balustered peg and flat-section bar.
£20 - £30

PB-T0114
Purse Bar
59mm
Knop ends, engraved.
£50 - £80

CP-3451
Gold Pendant
29mm
'Jesus walking on the waters' motif.
From £2,000

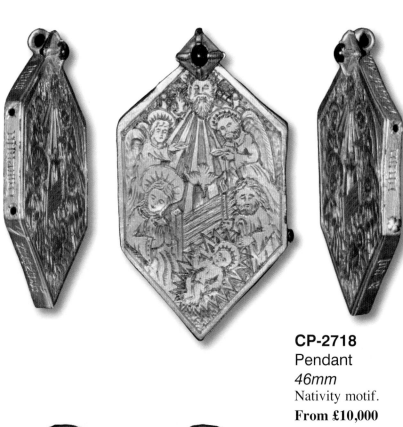

CP-2718
Pendant
46mm
Nativity motif.
From £10,000

CP-2817
Gold Posy
Pendant
20mm
Inscribed 'DIEU
PLERRA QANT
MEUIZ SERRA'
('When God
pleases we will be
one').
From £2,000

CP-9164
Silver-Gilt Pendant
33mm
Religious text 'AGLA' (abbreviation for 'Thine Is
The Power Throughout Endless Ages, O Lord') and
personal name 'Henri'.
£400 - £600

CP-34273
Gold Cross Pendant
62mm
Dark blue enamel with
nimbate Corpus Christi
and 'IC' (for Iesos
Christos 'Jesus Christ').
£500 - £800

CP-11795
Silver-Gilt
Pendant
33mm
Crucifixion scene
with 'INRI' Iesus
Nazarenus Rex
Iudaeorum'Jesus of
Nazareth, King of the
Jews'.
£200 - £300

CP-1456
Silver Pendant
Cross
33mm
Inscribed
'+IESVSNAS' (Jesus
of Nazareth) and
'ARIX – IVCI'.
£200 - £300

CP-44372
Gold Reliquary
Pendant
21mm
Cage with loop and
bone fragment inside.
£150 - £200

CP-30066
Silver Reliquary
Cross Pendant
78mm
Bifacial, obverse with
nimbate figure with
raised hands, 'MO' in
the hatched field; cross
to the reverse.
£200 - £300

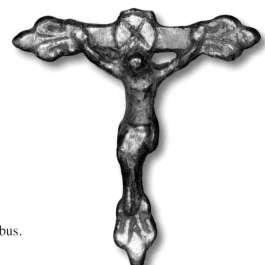

CP-16488
Silver-Gilt Pendant
30mm
Corpus Christi with nimbus.
£120 - £180

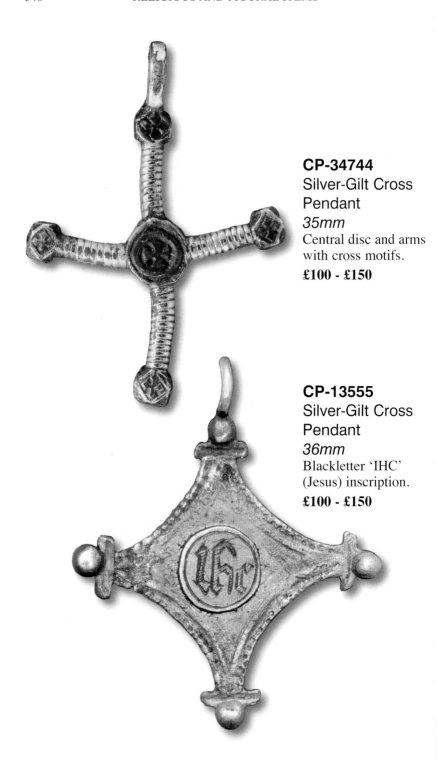

CP-34744
Silver-Gilt Cross
Pendant
35mm
Central disc and arms
with cross motifs.
£100 - £150

CP-13555
Silver-Gilt Cross
Pendant
36mm
Blackletter 'IHC'
(Jesus) inscription.
£100 - £150

CP-18128
Silver Cross Pendant
52mm
Florid bifacial plaque with bulb
finials.
£100 - £150

CP-21666
Silver Reliquary Cross Pendant
38mm
Nun's hinged cross pendant; Tudor type.
£80 - £120

CP-21662
Silver Cross Pendant
39mm
Radiating billets and
punched roundels.
£80 - £120

CP-19759
Silver Cross
Pendant
35mm
Incised 'IHC' for
IHCOC 'Jesus'.
£50 - £80

CP-T0140
Pendant
27mm
Enamelled quatrefoil
motif.
£100 – £150

CP-32157
Cross Pendant Set
34mm
Bronze pendants with
ring-and-dot ornament
on a wire ring.
£40 - £60

CP-32270
Monastic Cross Pendant
68mm
Wooden with recess
to the front.
£40 - £60

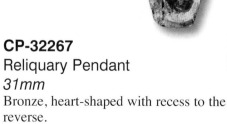

CP-32267
Reliquary Pendant
31mm
Bronze, heart-shaped with recess to the
reverse.
£40 - £60

PI-49910
Gold 'Book of St
Mark' Pendant
19mm
A miniature book with
two rectangular pages,
pin with polyhedral
head and attachment
loop.
£400 - £600

PI-49020
Lamp Bowl
95mm
Incised bands.
£80 - £120

PI-49936
Stylus
97mm
Incised cross.
£20 - £30

PI-52432
Stylus
82mm
Incised bird.
£30 - £40

PI-52209
Pilgrim Badge
27mm
Bird with head turned to raised wing.
£80 - £120

PI-52872
Coronation Pilgrim Badge
27mm
Henry VI wearing coronation robes and crown, right hand raised in blessing.
£50 - £80

PI-46560
Pin Badge Pair
30mm
Cross potent of the 'Equestrian Order of the Holy Sepulchre of Jerusalem'.
£50 - £80

PI-43786
Papal Bulla Seal Half
35mm
Bearded face beneath
'SPA' and to the reverse
the text 'R / [.]US /.V.'
(Pope Martin V).
£20 - £30

PI-46247
Angel
Pendant
46mm
Angel with
orb in one
hand.
£150 - £200

PI-45922
Pendant
28mm
Figures of archangels St Michael
and Gabriel. Byzantine type.
£20 - £30

We are accepting single entries and collections of coins and antiquities

Medieval The Congham Limoges Cross

Central London
Auction Venue

TimeLine Auctions Limited
The Court House
363 Main Road
Harwich, Essex
CO12 4DN

www.timelineauctions.com

+44 [0]1277 815121
enquiries@timelineauctions.com

SEAL MATRICES AND SEALS

Seal matrices were used to seal official documents and personal correspondence. They were originally the private property of powerful individuals who used them to signify assent and endorsement to the content of a document. These seals could be associated with an official position (chancellor, almoner, chamberlain, bishop, abbot, etc.) and implied administrative agreement. Aside from these official seals, which were received and passed on with the duties of the office, there were personal seals that remained the property of the individual and were used on personal communications.

Over time, the need arose for merchants to adopt personal seals when recording transactions and even for sealing the fastenings of bags of cargo. Symbols drawn from heraldry were adopted for these designs.

For personal correspondence, a series of standardised designs was used, such as the squirrel symbolising the secret or hidden nature of the message (in the same manner as a squirrel hides away nuts). The legend 'PRIVESV' meaning 'I am private' also occurs regularly on personal seals for correspondence.

Bullae is the name given to round, usually lead seals attached to correspondence from the Vatican on behalf of the pope. These follow a specific design, showing Saints Peter and Paul facing each other with a cross between, beneath the legends SPA (Sanctus Paulus) and SPE (Sanctus Petrus). The reverse has a legend in Roman capitals giving the pope's name followed by the letters 'PP' and the regnal number in Roman numerals.

Seal matrices are a popular collector's item. The heraldic content and the imagery are interesting as social documents, and the legends often point to named individuals whose lives may be traceable through other sources.

SS-45516
Silver 'ISABELLE of Malling' Heraldic Seal Matrix
23mm
Intaglio stag's head with hounds' heads, heater shield between the antlers with six martlets, legend '*S' ISABELLE : DE : MEAVLINGES'
From £1,500

SS-2481
Silver Seal Matrix
23mm
Text in Lombardic script 'X IHESUS : CRISTUS : AVEMAR' ('Jesus Christ, Hail Mary') and re-used Roman intaglio with winged Victory and cross-headed staff.
From £1,500

SS-9836
Silver Heraldic Seal Matrix
18mm
Inscribed 'SICILIE de ASK' (for Cecily Herbert of Usk).
From £1,000

SS-9789
Silver-Gilt Seal
Matrix
12mm
Inscribed 'Believe Me'.
£800 - £1,200

SS-48
'Sir Richard
Wortley' Silver-
Gilt Heraldic Seal
Matrix
19mm
Heater shield
diagonally divided
with three bezants,
three martlets in each
half.
£200 - £300

SS-3202
Silver Heraldic
Seal Matrix
25mm
Shield with
chequered chief
above a phoenix,
helmet with an
elaborate mantle,
phoenix above
battlements for the
crest.
£100 - £150

BS-38215

'King Robert the Bruce of Scotland and Dunfermline Abbey' Cokete Seal Matrix Pair

55mm

Obverse matrix depicting St Margaret in robe and crown with a sceptre, between two heater shields with Lombardic legend to the border 'S' COKETE REGALITATIS DE DVNFERMELYNN (cokete seal of the regality of Dunfermline); the reverse with heater shield depicting the royal arms of Scotland and border with the Lombardic legend 'ROBERTVS DEI GRACIA REX SCOTORVM (Robert, by the grace of God, king of the Scots) with floral ornament and quatrefoil stops.

From £50,000

BS-12815
'Cardinal Pedro Gonzalez De Mendoza' Heraldic Seal Matrix
57mm
Heater shield divided diagonally with hatched panels and the text 'AVE MAR' (for 'Hail Maria'), cardinal's hat with looped cords and tassels; text in seriffed capitals 'PETRUS GONZALEZ DE MENDOZA CARDINALIS HISPANIAE' (Cardinal Pedro Gonzalez de Mendoza of Spain).
From £1,000

BS-1813
Civic 'Berwick upon Tweed' Chamberlain's Seal Matrix
32mm
Hexafoil with a superimposed flag with three lions passant gardant and a bear beneath; legend + [...]IIIEII CAMERARII VILLE [B]RVICI ('(the seal of) the chamberlain of the town of Berwick').
£800 - £1,200

BS-3624
Heraldic Seal Matrix
30mm
Inscribed for Count Goffridi (Geoffrey).
£800 - £1,200

BS-34177
Seal Matrix with Cancelled Shield
29mm
Helmet with wolf-head crest and pansies, heater shield with hatched fess and deeply incised saltire cross overall; blackletter legend 'V DELNITICVOYEN'.

£300 - £500

BS-35762
Knight's Heraldic Seal Matrix
26mm
Chessman matrix with intaglio heater shield, quartered design of crosses potent and quatrefoils with central escutcheon, border with text 'S'LUGITE..EPA . MILITES Z DOCTORIS' (...knight and teacher).

£100 - £150

BS-42258
Large Heraldic Seal Matrix
31mm
Stamp seal matrix with heater shield and three thistles, hatched long cross; enigmatic legend 'S.MANAVT/E ET RNCIMI RAS'.
£100 - £150

BS-38702
Heraldic Seal Matrix
31mm
Heater shield with eagle, lion rampant supporters; legend in Lombardic script 'S+ SUM DO[...]ILI : M[.] N[.]NN[..]' (I am the seal of D...); Western European workmanship.
£30 - £50

BS-27580
Heraldic Seal Matrix
24mm
Heater-shaped seal matrix with lion rampant, two bands of text 'ET[.] ED[.]/MCHI'.
£50 - £80

BS-39208
Oval Seal Matrix
26mm
St Andrew facing, tied to
a saltire cross; Lombardic
script legend 'S' WILL'.
CAPELLANI + ANDREA
: PIE' (seal of William,
chaplain of St Andrew's).
£500 - £800

BS-31125
George and Dragon
Seal Matrix
25mm
Nimbate rider spearing a
dragon within a circular
border, band of text to the
outer edge.
£50 - £80

BS-31665
Seal Matrix
20mm
Squirrel motif.
£80 - £120

BS-46040
'Simon of Crécy' Seal Matrix
25mm
Stag before a two-branched tree, '*+S' SIMON·DE·CRECI' inscription for 'Seal of Simon of Crécy'.
£80 - £120

BS-12465
Seal Matrix
19mm
Crouching hare with incuse '*SOHOVTHCHIMWOT' enigmatic inscription.
£120 - £180

BS-46043
Teodorico Allegrini Seal Matrix
34mm
Wyvern in profile; '+MATRI TEDERICI ALLEGRINI IVD' inscription for master Teodorico Allegrini, judge; Italian type.
£70 - £100

BS-17331
Manticore Seal Matrix
35mm
Manticore rampant with
pelletted infill.
£200 - £300

BS-6650
Heraldic Seal Matrix
27mm
Heater shield with
rampant lion with text
'+SI VANCON CALOR'
in Lombardic script.
£100 - £150

BS-3626
Rampant Lion Seal
Matrix
32mm
Rampant lion with legend
+LEONIS DELIMENA
(the lion of ...) in Roman
lettering.
£200 - £300

BS-46049
'Tancred of Rosciano'
Seal Matrix
36mm
Rampant lion with '+S
TANCREDI DE ROSCIANO'
inscription for Tancred of
Rosciano;. Italian type.
£100 - £150

BS-46050
Jewish 'Lion Passant'
Seal Matrix
25mm
Lion passant; with incuse
legends S FOSON and Hebrew
עוריאלבריצחקצבי
('URIEL BAR YITZCHAK
TZVI', for Uriel the son of
Yitzchak Tzvi) inscriptions.
£100 - £150

BS-21023
Seal Matrix
27mm
Heater shield with lion and dragon
opposed, legend to the border
'IESVYSELDAMV/RVEL' (I am
the ...).
£80 - £120

BS-12289
'Bartholomew the Frepillonian' Lion and Unicorn Seal Matrix
19mm
Rampant lion and unicorn opposed within a band of Lombardic script '*BVRTELIMI LE PRAPELIOVN' ('Bartholomew the Frepillonian').
£120 - £180

BS-14470
Personal 'Seal of Reginald' Matrix
23mm
Lion and a bird fighting, '*SIGILL REGINALDI RTPE' (seal of Reginald of ...) legend around.
£120 - £180

BS-T0116
Seal Matrix
32mm
Lion mask and inscription 'SIGILLVM SECRET' for 'a seal of secrecy'.
£200 - £300

BS-46496
'Randulf Raribari' Seal Matrix
24mm
Bird in profile with
'+S'RADVLFI:RMRIBARI:'
inscription for Randulf or
Ralph.
£100 - £150

BS-23328
Quatrefoil Seal Matrix
31mm
Cross potent on a rectangular
field, running animals to the
arms; Spanish type.
£50 - £80

BS-12782
Crusader Seal Matrix
31mm
Inscribed for Stephen of Cyprus.
£100 - £150

BS-44947
'Ranulf of Bobernart'
Seal Matrix
29mm
Fleur-de-lys with pellets
and two saltire crosses,
double chevron below with
legend '+S' RAOVL DV
BOBERNART:' (seal of
Ranulf of Bobernart).
£80 - £120

BS-12519
'Simon (of) Highbury'
Hexagonal Seal Matrix
22mm
Fleur with inscription
'+S'SIMONIHIVBERI' in
Roman letters for 'seal of
Simon (of) Highbury'.
£80 - £120

BS-37507
Seal Matrix with Boat
31mm
Boat with Lombardic
script (?) legend to the
border 'SPEROGOON
ETSCOVETA'; Catalan
type.
£200 - £300

BS-46039
'Roger Trule' Seal Matrix
18mm
Single-masted ship with
rigging of six lines and
three-tailed pennant,
'*S' ROGERI·TRVLE'·,
inscription for Roger Trule.
£80 - £120

BS-31804
Seal Matrix with
Horseshoe
24mm
Horseshoe with surrounding
enigmatic legend
'+SPERRESONLEMAR[...]'.
£80 - £120

BS-19361
Seal Matrix
24mm
Crowned 'R' motif.
£80 - £120

BS-11997
Seal Matrix
24mm
Inscribed for Alexander of
Bergia.
£200 - £300

BS-42588
Stamp Seal Matrix
30mm
Human figure and crescent.
£20 - £30

BS-41490
Seal Matrix with
Triangle and Star
44mm
Central starburst, triangular
border with enigmatic
Lombardic script legend
'S'MARIROIH:DE:
ESPELO'.
£300 - £500

BS-12516
Trial Piece
38mm
From a seal-
maker's
workshop.
£80 - £120

BS-T0118
Wool Seal
44mm
Inscription 'Harlem
Alnager' in blackletter.
£20 - £30

BS-9946
Seal Matrix
65mm
From the office of Pope
Urban V; attributable to
Cardinal Adam Easton.

From £1,500

BS-9549
Priory Seal
Matrix
52mm
Inscribed for
St Victor of
Marseilles.
From £1,200

BS-46489
'Hugh De La Croix of
Pershore Abbey' Seal
Matrix
29mm
Tall cross with triangular base,
inscribed 's' HVGOM DE LA
CROYS DE PERE'inscription
for Hugo (or Hugh) de la Croix
('of the cross') of Pershore
Abbey (Worcestershire).
£150 - £200

BS-46037
'Raul, Master of Saint Esperit' Seal Matrix
37mm
Cross of Lorraine; with inscription ' +S' RAOVL MAITRE DOVSAINT ESPERIT' (for Raul, master of Saint Esperit); French type.
£100 - £150

BS-30004
'St Augustine's Abbey' Almoner's Seal Matrix
35mm
The Virgin Mary holding the Christ child enthroned beneath a gothic arch, with supplicant figure kneeling below with inscription +S' ELEMOSINARII SCI AVGVSTI CANT (seal of the almoner of St Augustine of Canterbury) in Lombardic script.
From £2,000

BS-44449
Abbey Seal Matrix with
Resurrection Scene
57mm
Christ rising from the tomb
flanked by angels with a
sleeping guard beneath,
inscription to the border in
blackletter script 'SIGILLUM
SAINTE SUIULM S AUSTR'
(seal of Saint ...).
£1,200 - £1,800

BS-4885
'Bishop of Nottingham'
Seal Matrix
59mm
Crowned royal armorial
with supporters, inscription
OFFICIA/LITAT/ARCNNAT/
NOT (by authority of the
office of the archdeaconry of
Nottingham); to the border the
inscription SIGILLUM: REGIE:
MAIESTIE: AD.CAVSAS:
ECCLESIASTIC[A]S (seal of
his majesty the king for church
matters).
From £1,500

BS-39196
Madonna and Child
Seal Matrix
46mm
Madonna and Child within
a trefoil arch with cross
above, a smaller arch
below between towers
with supplicant figure and
Lombardic script legend
'S' CONVENTVS F R M
PREDICATORUM VRG'
M' (seal of the convention
... of the preachers of the
Virgin Mary?).
£500 - £800

BS-46503
'Nicholas the Tanner of
Wallingford' Seal Matrix
32mm
Mother and Child between
pylons and praying monk
below, '*S' NICOLI LE
TANNVR DE WALI'
inscription (for Nicholas
the tanner of Wallingford,
Berkshire).
£200 - £300

BS-46505
'Clerk Walter de Newent'
Seal Matrix
30mm
Mother and Child under
canopy and praying monk
below, '*S' WALTERI
DE NEWENT CLERICI'
inscription (for clerk Walter
of Newent, Gloucestershire).
£200 - £300

BS-39205
'Gabriel and Mary
Annunciation' Seal Matrix
31mm
Double arch with column
and abbey buildings above, a
winged male figure (Gabriel)
in one arch addressing a
facing robed female (Mary)
in the other, supplicant below
with hands raised; Lombardic
script legend 'MISS:EST
GABRIEL AD MARI'
(Gabriel is sent to Mary).
£300 - £400

BS-46490
'St Mary Pray for Thy Servant' Monastic Seal Matrix
31mm
Mother and Child under arch with praying monk below under gothic trefoil arch, 'ORA PRO FAMVLO SCA MARIA TVO' inscription (for 'St Mary pray for thy servant').
£200 - £300

BS-39203
'Queen of Mercy' Seal Matrix
35mm
Madonna and Child and supplicant figure praying beneath an arch, Lombardic script legend '+SALVE REGINA MISERICORDE' (save [me] o queen of mercy).
£200 - £300

BS-46563
'Clerk William of Calvomote' Seal Matrix
32mm
Mother and Child with sun and crescent moon, kneeling monk before, '*S' WILL'I:DE: CALVOMOTE:CL'ICI' inscription (for clerk William of Calvomote).

£200 - £300

BS-6345
'Madonna and Child' Seal Matrix
32mm
Madonna and Child and supplicant figure praying beneath an arch, Lombardic script text '*AVGMARIAGRATIAPE' (for Ave Maria gratia plena 'Hail Mary, full of grace').

£100 - £150

BS-39542
Seal Matrix with
Madonna and Child
25mm
Madonna and Child with
Lombardic script legend
'AVE MARIA GRACIA'.
£80 - £120

BS-46488
'St Laurence of
Rome' Seal Matrix
31mm
St Laurence seated on
abbey roof holding
book and gridiron,
monk praying under
pointed arch, '*PROME
LAVREN PE TOSTES ID
HOMHABTI' inscription
for 'pray for Lawrence
roasted by the inhuman'.
£300 - £500

BS-4632
Heraldic Seal Matrix
47mm
Facing bust within a lancet arch
with spires, shield with two lions
passant and a quarter with a lion
rampant within a tressy border;
inscription 'S' G.MATI.DEO/DE
SABOLIO*'.

£500 - £800

BS-39207
'St Peter' Seal Matrix
31mm
St Peter facing, holding a book
and a key, stars and crescents
in the field, Lombardic script
legend 'TV ES PETRVS ET
SVP HAC PETRA' (you are
the rock and on this rock.

£400 - £600

BS-4858
Seal Matrix
38mm
Standing saint within a
lancet arch with helmet,
cross-headed staff, a small
figure and a bird ; enigmatic
inscription in Lombardic
capitals '[ ]PER OTE
RVCELIB'.
£150 - £200

BS-4282
Seal Matrix
52mm
Inscribed for St Michael's
Monastery.
£100 - £150

BS-39195
'Alexander of Thorpe' Vesica Seal Matrix
33mm

Robed figure beneath a tracery arch with raised hand, chalice on altar before, Lombardic script legend 'S' ALEXSANDRI DE TORPI' (seal of Alexander of Thorpe [-in-Balne]).

£200 - £300

BS-54361
Vesica Personal Seal Matrix with Pelican
27mm

A bronze vesica seal matrix with strap and loop to the reverse, central intaglio motif 'pelican in her piety' (pelican with gouts of blood, three nestlings and tree), surrounding legend '*IOESVSEL DE ANOVOLEL'.

£50 - £80

BS-34482
'Agnus Dei' Vesica Seal
27mm
Lamb with cross above its back and Lombardic legend 'DENIS CSTOF' (Dennis Christopher?).
£100 - £150

BS-4857
'Robert of Moravia' Knight's Seal Matrix
41mm
Tree and running hound with star above its head, inscription in Lombardic capitals '+S'ROBTI:DE:MORAVIA: CAPPLI' for 'the seal of Robert of Moravia'.
£200 - £300

BS-46493
'Richard of Lekche' Seal
Matrix
31mm
Wyvern in profile with '+S'
RICARD'.DE LEKCHE'
inscription (for Richard of
Lekche).
£80 - £120

BS-46502
'William the Chaplain'
Seal Matrix
31mm
Pelican in her piety (pelican
with three nestlings) and
'+S':WILELMI:capellan'
inscription (for William the
Chaplain).
£200 - £300

BS-46504
'Richard of Rizer' Seal Matrix
37mm
Pelican in her piety with '+S' RICARDI DE RIZER' inscription (for Richard of Rizer (possibly Ryther, North Yorkshire)).
£200 - £300

BS-38194
'Pelican In Her Piety' Seal Matrix
29mm
Pelican in her piety with legend '*SIMILIS SVM PELICAN' (I am like the pelican).
£100 - £150

BS-46057
Saint-Hippolyte Seal Matrix
42mm
Pelican in her piety and '+S.:A:CVRATI:SCI:POLITI' inscription (for the curate of Saint-Hippolyte in Lorraine, France?).
£120 - £180

BS-21557
'Pelican In Piety' Seal Matrix
25mm
Pelican in her piety with '*TIMETEDEVE' ('fear God') inscription.
£50 - £80

BS-12518
'Fear the Lord' Seal
Matrix
25mm
Pelican in her piety with
'*TIMETE DOMINVM'
in Roman letters ('fear the
Lord').
£80 - £120

BS-26742
'Robert Fraving'
Hawking Seal Matrix
30mm
Hawk taking its prey with
'+S'ROBERTIFRAVNG'
inscription (for 'seal of
Robert Fraving').
£120 - £180

BS-11161
'France(s) of
Leicester' Seal Matrix
28mm
Pair of birds with legend
'+FRANCE:LECETC*'.
£100 - £150

BS-11998
'Felicie of (Sutton)
Bassett' Seal Matrix
29mm
Standing bird with legend
'SIGILL.FELICIE.BASSET.'
with crescent (for 'seal of
Felicie of (Sutton) Bassett').
£80 - £120

BS-7832
Seal Matrix
30mm
Plant with recurved
leaves, text in
Lombardic capitals
'*SIGIL[..]
ETSECRETICAP
ETULI'.
£50 - £80

BS-19375
Seal Matrix Group
21-25mm
One discoid with
central rosette
and surrounding
legend; one vesica-
shaped with central
bird motif, legend
'CREDETE.C.HIX'
to the border.
£100 - £150

BS-14203
Seal Matrix Group
28-29mm
One with fleur-de-lys motif
and legend '+S'NICHOL[.]
WRTHISSTED' (seal of
Noicholas of ?); one with bird
motif and legend '+SIGILLV.
SECRETI' (seal of a secret).
£80 - £120

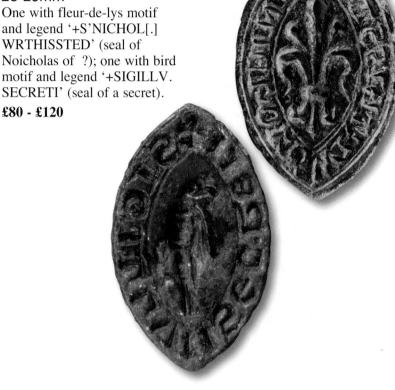

BS-9514
Vesica Seal Matrix
28mm
Bird of prey with
legend in Lombardic
capitals '*FRANCE
VEGE TEGE' (for
'frange, lege, tege'
'break this, read it and
cover it').
£50 - £80

BS-2717
Heraldic Seal
Matrix
39mm
Arms of Sir John
Bridsale.
£1,000 - £1,500

BS-5845
Heraldic Seal
Matrix
33mm
Inscribed for
Renard of
Themericourt.
£500 - £800

BS-6248
'Sulyarde Family'
Knight's Seal
Matrix
26mm
Heater shield
with chevron
pelletty between
three pheons,
inscribed '+S'
RADODEHIIOSET'
in Lombardic
capitals.
£200 - £300

BS-46478
Knight's Seal Matrix
34mm
Helmet with dog-head crest and cross; shield with bend and three cross crosslets, label overall; German legend ' + SIEL + IOHANIO HANU +' (seal of Johann son of Johann?) with fronds between; German type.
From £500

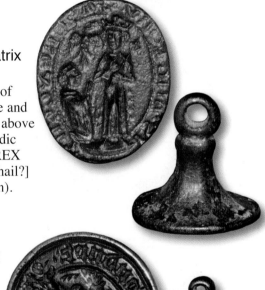

BS-39197
'King of the English Nation' Oval Seal Matrix
20mm
Standing crowned figure of the king holding a sceptre and with an eagle to his side, above a figure praying, Lombardic script legend 'A[V?E?] REX GENTIS ANGLORV' ([hail?] king of the English nation).
£300 - £500

BS-36373
'Pierre Condurt' Seal Matrix
40mm
Heraldic helmet with displayed mantle, canted shield, flowers in the field; the crest a stag emerging from a thicket, the shield with lion passant below three cinquefoils, blackletter text 'PIERRECONDURT'; French type.
£500 - £800

BS-990
'Sir William de Lisle of Rougemont' Seal Matrix
36mm
Castle with a superimposed shield of arms (martlet between two chevrons) and forequarters of a horned bull.
£200 - £300

BS-46036
'William of Torot' Seal Matrix
22mm
Three-turretted tower, barred, with '+S':GVILLANNE· D'LATOROT inscription (for 'seal of William of Torot').
£100 - £150

BS-36016
Heraldic Seal Matrix
25mm
Heater shield divided with left side plain, right side with seven bars, legend '*[..] GAVD .MISE .MEI.' ('... have mercy on me').
£50 - £80

BS-30046
Seal Matrix
27mm
Bishop in robes and mitre holding a crozier, blessing a kneeling monk
holding a palm branch, with 'D g diitnir p de S Antim' blackletter
legend (for 'd[ei] g[ratia] diitnir p[resbyter] de S Antim[o]' 'By the
grace of God, Diitnir Presbyter of St Antimo Abbey'). Italian type.
£400 - £600

BS-46497
'The Rood' Seal Matrix
21mm
Rood cross with Christ crucified against a cross-hatched and dotted
background with kneeling monk praying below within a gothic arch,
enigmatic '+W.DEBE.TRIBVE.ELICADL' CIFLVE' inscription
(perhaps Caldwell).
£200 - £300

BS-33986
Seal Matrix with Corpus Christi
28mm
Crucifixion scene with Corpus Christi and two flanking figures, legend to the border 'IESVS [.]+CHRISTVS' (Jesus Christ).
£80 - £120

BS-46038
'Christ Crucified' Seal Matrix
23mm
Christ crucified with figure each side; inscribed *IESVS NAZERENVS ('Jesus of Nazareth').
£100 - £150

BS-39200
'Haldard' Corpus Christi Oval Seal Matrix
33mm
Crucifixion in one arch and Madonna and Child in the other, robed supplicant beneath with chalice, Lombardic script legend 'MATER QV[...] HALDARD' (mother [of god?] ...haldard).
£100 - £150

BS-46494
'Jesus Is My Love' Seal Matrix
18mm

Christogram 'IHC' with three crosses from the crucifixion of Christ at Calvary, inscribed 'EST AMORE MEV' (for 'Jesus is my love').

£80 - £120

BS-46500
'Thank You Jesus' Seal Matrix
20mm

Profile male bust (representing Jesus?) with '*IESVS MERCI' inscription (for 'thank you Jesus'). French type.

£100 - £150

BS-39199
'John of Messingham' Oval Seal Matrix
23mm

Madonna and Child with tree within an arch, lateral towers and stars above, kneeling supplicant in panel beneath, Lombardic script legend 'S'IOH'IS DE MESSINGHAM' ('seal of John of Messingham').

£200 - £300

BS-14451
Seal Matrix
23mm
Madonna and Child motif.
£100 - £150

BS-46491
'Hail Mary Full of Grace' Seal Matrix
22mm
Mother and Child with two palm fronds behind, '*AVE MARIA GRACIA' inscription (for 'hail Mary [full of] grace').
£100 - £150

BS-40731
'Maria Gratia Plena' Seal Matrix
20mm
Mary seated with Child, supplicant kneeling to one side, with legend 'MARIA GRATIA PLENA' in the quadrants.
£50 - £80

BS-39201
'St Catherine' Oval Seal
Matrix
27mm
Facing female figure holding a spoked and spiked wheel, a frond to each side, Lombardic script legend '*SAVNCA CATERINA' (Saint Catherine).
£200 - £300

BS-39202
'St Catherine' Circular Seal
Matrix
29mm
Quatrefoil with a tressure of arches, facing female figure with a spiked wheel in her left hand and robed kneeling figure praying at her side, Lombardic script legend 'CATINA : VIRGO : DIVINA : CLEMENT[IS]S[I]MA' (Catherine the most merciful divine virgin).
£200 - £300

BS-39198
'St Helena' Oval
Seal Matrix
26mm
Robed standing female
figure holding a cross,
head inclined towards a
kneeling figure praying
in a field of trefoils,
Lombardic script legend
'*SCHELENA.PRO.
ME.ORA' (Saint Helena
pray for me).
£200 - £300

BS-39206
'St Stephen'
Circular Seal Matrix
34mm
Standing robed figure
holding stones with
fronds in the field,
Lombardic script
legend '*SANCTVS-
STEFANVS' (Saint
Stephen).
£400 - £600

BS-32340
'John Randolf' Seal
Matrix
29mm
Standing figure and
a smaller figure with
raised arms, stars in the
field, legend '*S' IOH.
RANDULF' (seal of
John Randolf).
£150 - £200

SEAL MATRICES AND SEALS

BS-39204
'St John the Baptist' Oval Seal Matrix
29mm
Standing figure of St John within an arcade with trefoils and tracery with kneeling supplicant figure before, Lombardic script legend 'ECCEXAGNVSXDEI' (behold, the lamb of god').

£50 - £80

BS-39209
'St John the Baptist' Oval Seal Matrix
28mm
Facing nimbate figure of St John standing with frond and holding a miniature lamb-and-flag icon, Lombardic script legend 'ECCE AGNVS D[?]EI' (behold, the lamb of God).

£200 - £300

BS-31128
Figural Seal Matrix
18mm
Standing figure with raised arms within a border of radiating lines; Eastern European type.

£30 - £50

BS-29077
Pendant Seal Matrix
24mm
Central pellet with foliage and cross above, Lombardic script 'IhC' (the Christogram) and '*CSTAMORN[.]/' enigmatic legend to the border.
£70 - £100

BS-6153
Lamb Of God Seal Matrix
23mm
Regardant lamb with flag within a circular border, the legend 'ECCE AGNUS.DEI' ('behold, the lamb of God') in Lombardic script.
£100 - £150

BS-1816
Lamb of God Seal Matrix
25mm
Quatrefoil decoration with lamb and flag beneath a star, 'S[...] AGNUS DEI' inscription (Lamb of God).
£80 - £120

BS-33987
Lamb of God
Seal Matrix
21mm
Lamb with cross
and flag (Agnus
Dei) and legend
'RANVLFRICL
[...]' (Ranulf...).
£30 - £50

BS-21021
Lamb of God
Seal Matrix
21mm
Agnus Dei with
large flag and legend
'ECCE AGNVS
DEI' (behold the
Lamb of God).
£50 - £80

BS-46054
'Henry Ralph
John of Culham'
Seal Matrix
21mm
Squirrel couchant
holding nut in
mouth, inscribed
'*S' HEI'
RAL' IOH'S
DE CVLHAM
MILNE' (for
Henry Ralph John,
miller at Culham,
Oxfordshire).
£100 - £150

BS-11888
Squirrel Seal
Matrix
19mm
Squirrel within a
border with the
enigmatic text
'*ICRAEENOTIS'.
£50 - £80

BS-14448
Squirrel Seal
Matrix
17mm
Squirrel sitting
with '*PRIVE
SV' (I am private)
legend.
£50 - £80

BS-21556
Squirrel Seal
Matrix
14mm
Squirrel within an
octahedral surround
with '+EAEDE--'
text in angles.
£50 - £80

BS-21558
Squirrel Seal
Matrix
19mm
Seated squirrel
with enigmatic
'*IERAHENOTIS'
inscription.
£70 - £100

BS-44
Stag Seal Matrix
31mm
Antlered sacrificial
stag with dappled
hide lying down,
cross-headed banner
with 'Z' across
the pole with a
quatrefoil to one side,
inscription reading
'S' RICARDI TAS'
(seal of Richard ...).
£200 - £300

BS-46492
'Richard Raner
of Dorking' Seal
Matrix
17mm
Stag's head with
cross pattée between
antlers, sun and
crescent moon at
sides, inscribed '*S'
RICI RANER DE
DORH[or K?]YNG'
(for Richard Raner of
Dorking, Surrey).
£120 - £180

BS-35974
Stag's Head
Seal Matrix
20mm
Stag with cross
between the antlers,
associated with both
St Hubert of Lièges
and St Eustace;
legend '*IESVS
MERCI' (thanks
[be to] Jesus).
£20 - £30

BS-6250
Seal Matrix
20mm
Hare and bird
beneath the legend
'SOHOV' (a
hunting cry).
£100 - £150

BS-8776
Stamp Seal
Matrix
20mm
Hare riding a
hound and blowing
a hunting horn
surrounded by
text in Lombardic
capitals 'ALONE I
RIDE A REVERE'.
£80 - £120

BS-45252
Rabbit Riding Dog Seal Matrix
21mm
Rabbit riding a dog (?) and enigmatic legend '*S' OHOAROBEN'.
£80 - £120

BS-7339
Heraldic Seal Matrix
19mm
Pelletted band above a rider blowing a hunting horn.
£50 - £80

BS-46053
'I am a Lion' Seal Matrix
18mm
Lion couchant with hare above between two branches, 'LEOSV' inscription ('I am a lion').
£80 - £120

BS-46055
'I am Private and Afterwards Known' Seal Matrix
22mm
Tree with three branches with a lion dormant below with '*PREVE SV POV CONV' inscription (for 'I am private and afterwards known').
£50 - £80

BS-19622
Seal Matrix
19mm
Rampant lion and band of text '*SVM LLEO FORTIS' (I am as strong as a lion).
£80 - £120

BS-46499
'Lion Mask Seal Matrix
20mm
Facing mask of a lion within a ten-pointed tracery, enigmatic letters(?) or symbols in the angles.
£80 - £120

BS-44901
'Nicholas of Stoneteli'
Seal Matrix
21mm
Rampant human-headed lion
with legend '*S'NICHI.D'
STONETELI' for 'Seal of
Nicholas of Stone (S)Tile?'.
£150 - £200

BS-14468
Seal Matrix with
Rampant Lion
21mm
Rampant lion
with 'SVM LEO
FORTIS'legend (I am
as strong as a lion).
£150 - £200

BS-33985
Seal Matrix with
Rampant Lion
26mm
Rampant lion with
the legend '*SVM
LEO FORTIS' (I am
as strong as a lion).
£80 - £120

BS-22734
Seal Matrix with
Leopard
22mm
Rampant leopard
with '*S'-M-
EOHORRIS'
inscription
(blundered sum leo
fortis 'I am as strong
as a lion').
£40 - £60

BS-26759
Seal Matrix with
Peacock Handle
38mm
Handle formed as a
regardant peacock,
motif of regardant
beast with open jaws
and raised tail.
£80 - £120

BS-46052
'William Cokhead' Double Seal Matrix
15-22mm
Cock's head with '*S' WILLAM COKHEAD '(for William Cockhead), circular secondary face with cross within a pentagram.
£120 - £180

BS-4281
Eagle Seal Matrix
30mm
Spread eagle surrounded by groups of four points with '+F.AMONI NOVI.HONAR.T' inscription.
£80 - £120

BS-47405
Eagle Seal Matrix
17mm
Eagle with spread wings and legend '*PRIVE SV' (I am private).
£50 - £80

BS-12290
Eagle Seal Matrix
19mm
Eagle with spread wings, legend in display capitals '*PRIVESVM' ('I am private').
£50 - £80

BS-46495
Seal Matrix
16mm
Large fleur-de-lys with arrowhead terminal to central element, with '*S' WILLI RAPVN' inscription (for William of Ripon, Yorkshire).
£100 - £150

BS-46498
Seal Matrix
19mm
Single-masted ship with pairs of rigging lines and cross to the masthead breaking the enigmatic inscription 'CHOLI MILOEH'.
£200 - £300

BS-T0117
Seal Matrix
25mm
Anchor motif.
£100 - £150

BS-46044
Seal Matrix
22mm
Loom shuttle with
foliage at sides, '*S'
LOIS*CHAVCIE'
inscription (for Louis
Chaucie). French type.
£80 - £120

BS-46045
Seal Matrix
25mm
Balance scale with
'[U?Q?]UOTO
S AUGUSTIN'
blackletter
inscription (for
St Augustine).
Continental type.
£100 - £150

BS-46501
Seal Matrix
19mm
Merchant's mark of a cross-headed staff with three-tailed pennant surmounting a pyramid, '*MATHEEVA CHIDRE' inscription (for the merchant Matthew Chider).
£100 - £150

BS-31806
Circular Seal Matrix
26mm
Axe with enigmatic 'XXOVEL BREXXET' inscription.
£80 - £120

BS-21019
Seal Matrix
24mm
With merchant's mark and symbols with incuse '*IOHES* KVRTVN*' inscription (for 'John Kirton').
£150 - £200

BS-22733
Seal Matrix
26mm
With hexafoil and
star.
£100 - £150

BS-30417
Merchant's Seal
Matrix
38mm
Two pelleted borders
with arm and cross,
enigmatic legend
'+VIC:HACOAVIM'.
£80 - £120

BS-17333
'Stephen the
Goldsmith' Seal
Matrix
19mm
Profile bust with cross
and text 'S'STEPH'[I]
AVRIFABRI' (for
'sigillum Stephani
Aurifabri' 'seal
of Stephen the
goldsmith'.
£100 - £150

BS-42520
Double-Headed
Heraldic Seal
Matrix
26mm
One head with
merchant's mark
of a doubled cross
with short lateral
angled bar beneath
each crossbar;
the other head
with similar mark
and 'S' IONIS
DE CO[M?]E[.]'
inscription (seal of
John of ?).
£100 - £150

BS-3636
Epigraphic Seal
Matrix
26mm
Heater shield
with capital 'M'
in Lombardic
script, legend '+
MABREY DE
BRAINNE'.
£80 - £120

LS-18056
Alexander III
Papal Bulla Seal
35mm
Saints Peter and
Paul to one face,
inscribed ALEX /
ANDER / PP III to
the other in three
lines; deliberately
compressed at sides.
£80 - £120

LS-19366
Clement III
Papal Bulla
39mm
Saints Peter
and Paul to one
face, 'SPA.S[..]',
reverse inscribed
'CL[.]/MENS/PP
III'.
£50 - £80

LS-8513
Honorius III
Papal Bulla
42mm
Saints Peter
and Paul to one
face, 'SPA.
SPE' legend,
reverse inscribed
'HONO/RIVS/
P.P.III'.
£80 - £120

LS-6682
Gregory IX
Papal Bulla
42mm
Saints Peter and
Paul to one face,
'SPA.SPE' legend,
reverse inscribed
'GRE/GORIVS/PP.
VIIII'.
£80 - £120

LS-8486
Gregory IX
Papal Bulla
40mm
Saints Peter and
Paul to one face,
'SPA.SPE' legend,
reverse inscribed
'GRE/GORIVS/
P.P.VIIII'.
£80 - £120

LS-19370
Gregory IX
Papal Bulla
38mm
Saints Peter and
Paul to one face,
'SPA.SPE' legend,
reverse inscribed
'GRE/GORIVS/PP.
VIIII'.
£80 - £120

LS-22754
Martin IV Papal Bulla
39mm
Saints Peter and Paul to one face, 'SPA.SPE' legend, reverse inscribed 'MAR/TINVS/PP. IIII'.
£50 - £80

LS-2045
Urban IV Papal Bulla
40mm
Saints Peter and Paul to one face, 'SPA.SPE' legend, reverse inscribed 'VR/BANVS /PP IIII'.
£50 - £80

LS-520
John XXII Papal Bulla
36mm
Saints Peter and Paul to one face, 'SPA.SPE' legend, reverse inscribed 'IOH /ANNES /PP XXII'.
£50 - £80

LS-32195
Boniface IX Papal
Bulla
36mm
Saints Peter and Paul
to one face, 'SPA.SPE'
legend, reverse inscribed
'BONI / FATIVS /
P.P.VIII'.
£50 - £80

LS-19619
Seal Matrix
37mm
Hammer motif, pellets
and text to the border
'+S'GALFRID.FAB' for
'Sigillum Galfridi Fabricii'
(Seal of Geoffrey the
Smith).
£20 - £30

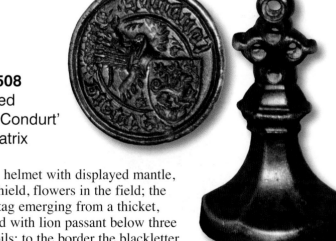

LS-22755
Seal Matrix
Pair
25-33mm
A pair of lead seal
matrices comprising: one
annular with radiating
arms and impressed text
'+S'MARGERICREYGIBELOT'
(seal of Margery...); one discoid
with strap to the reverse, text
'S'TERGVL[.]OMVIGIO[...].
£30 - £50

BS-48508
Inscribed
'Pierre Condurt'
Seal Matrix
40mm
Heraldic helmet with displayed mantle,
canted shield, flowers in the field; the
crest a stag emerging from a thicket,
the shield with lion passant below three
cinquefoils; to the border the blackletter
text 'pierre condurt'; Continental
workmanship.
£300 - £500

BS-49904
Heraldic Seal
Matrix
34mm
Intaglio square
heraldic arms
divided vertically,
with four birds
above a chevron,
three birds below
and three crenellated
bars; Continental
type.
£80 - £120

BS-49905
Inscribed Seal
Matrix
18mm
Intaglio lion
couchant with hare
and two branches,
'LEOSV' ('I am a
lion') inscription.
£80 - £120

BS-49067
Seal Matrix with
Bird
21mm
Bird and foliage with
enigmatic legend
'*VISQVIMA
VETRENMECREI'.
£80 - £120

BS-49066
Seal Matrix with Beast
20mm
Intaglio animal with fronds.
£50 - £80

BS-49901
Wolf and Hound Seal Matrix
28mm
Intaglio arms with foliage depicting a wolf and collared hound with collared hound crest; incuse 'ZIOFFIE GRANOWSKA Z DVBNICZE' inscription (for Lady Sofia Granowska of Dubnicze, Poland).
£100 - £150

BS-49902
Tancred Of Rosciano Seal Matrix
36mm
Intaglio rampant lion with '+S TANCREDI DE ROSCIANO' inscription (for Tancred of Rosiano).
£80 - £120

BS-49074
Inscribed Seal Matrix
17mm
Grid motif with surrounding legend '+PRIVESV' (I am private).
£50 - £80

BS-48119
Inscribed Seal Matrix
22mm
Intaglio Agnus Dei, Lombardic text '+S' IOHAN DE HOVTONE' (Seal of John of Hoveton).
£80 - £120

BS-49073
Inscribed Seal Matrix
20mm
Intaglio trefoil and bird-heads, '*IESVSEL DANOR' (I am ...) legend.
£50 - £80

BS-46563
'Clerk William Of Calvomote' Vesica Seal Matrix
32mm
Intaglio Mother and Child with sun and crescent moon above, kneeling monk, incuse *S' WILL'I: DE: CALVOMOTE: CL'ICI' (for Clerk William of Calvomote).

£180 - £240

BS-44899
Heater Seal Matrix
27mm
Heater shield with lion and dragon opposed, pellets in the field and legend to the border 'IESVYSELDAMV/RVEL' (I am the ?).

£80 - £120

OTHER BOOKS PUBLISHED

Advanced Detecting *Norfolk Wolf (John Lynn)* 250mm x 190mm, 108 pages

Beginner's Guide to Metal Detecting *Julian Evan-Hart & David Stuckey* 250mm x 190mm, 92 pages

Benet's Artefacts 3rd Edition *Brett Hammond* 220mm x 140mm hardback, 864 pages

British Artefacts Volume 1 – Early Anglo-Saxon *Brett Hammond* A4, 132 pages

British Artefacts Volume 2 – Middle Saxon & Viking *Brett Hammond* A4, 148 pages

British Artefacts Volume 3 – Late Saxon, Viking & Norman *Brett Hammond* A4, 128 pages

British Buttons 19th-20th Century *Dennis Blair* A5, 92 pages

Buttons & Fasteners 500BC-AD1840 *Gordon Bailey* 250mm x 190mm, 116 pages

Buckles 1250-1800 *Ross Whitehead* A4, 128 pages

Celtic & Roman Artefacts *Nigel Mills* A4, 152 pages

Cleaning Coins & Artefacts *David Villanueva* 250mm x 190mm, 116 pages

Detector Finds 1 *Gordon Bailey* A4, 100 pages

Detector Finds 2 *Gordon Bailey* A4, 100 pages

Detector Finds 3 *Gordon Bailey* A4, 96 pages

Detector Finds 4 *Gordon Bailey* A4, 100 pages

Detector Finds 5 *Gordon Bailey* A4, 100 pages

Detector Finds 6 *Gordon Bailey* A4, 116 pages

Detector Finds 7 *Gordon Bailey* A4, 125 pages

www.greenlightpublishing.co.uk

GREENLIGHT PUBLISHING

History of Medieval Coinage in England *Richard Kelleher* A4, 216 pages

History of Roman Coinage in Britain *Sam Moorhead* A4, 224 pages

Leaden Tokens & Tallies *Ted Fletcher* 250mm x 190mm, 116 pages

Medieval Artefacts *Nigel Mills* A4, 116 pages

Medieval English Groats *Ivan Buck* A4, 68 pages

Metal Detecting – All you need to know to get started
Dave Crisp 235mm x 150mm, 150+ pages

Pottery in Britain 4000BC to AD1900 *Lloyd Laing* 250mm x 190mm, 136 pages

Reading Beaches *Ted Fletcher* A5, 80 pages

Reading Land *Ted Fletcher* A5, 100 pages

Reading Tidal Rivers *Ted Fletcher* A5, 84 pages

Roman Buckles and Military Fittings *Andrew Appels & Stuart Laycock* 250mm x 190mm, 284 pages

Roman Coins and Their Values – Volumes 1-5 *David R. Sear* 225mm x 145mm hardback

Site Research *David Villanueva* 250mm x 190mm, 160 pages

Successful Detecting Sites *David Villanueva* 250mm x 190mm, 238 pages

Saxon & Viking Artefacts *Nigel Mills* A4, 108 pages

The Tribes & Coins of Celtic Britain *Rainer Pudill & Clive Eyre* 250mm x 190mm, 84 pages

Tokens & Tallies 1850-1950 *Ted Fletcher* 250mm x 190mm, 100+ pages

Tokens & Tallies Through the Ages *Ted Fletcher* 250mm x 190mm, 100 pages

  ☎ **01376 521900**